MICHAEL SERVETUS
HUMANIST AND MARTYR

BY

JOHN F. FULTON

WITH A BIBLIOGRAPHY OF HIS WORKS
AND CENSUS OF KNOWN COPIES

BY

MADELINE E. STANTON

HERBERT REICHNER

NEW YORK 21, N. Y.

1953

PRINTED IN THE UNITED STATES

MICHAEL SERVETUS

PUBLICATION NO. 22

HISTORICAL LIBRARY • YALE MEDICAL LIBRARY

AND

DEPARTMENT OF THE HISTORY OF MEDICINE

YALE UNIVERSITY

Servetus in prison. Bronze statue by Clotilde Roch erected in 1908 at Annemasse
and torn down by order of the Germans on 13 September 1941.

TO THE MEMORY

of Three Servetus Scholars

HENRI TOLLIN

ALEXANDER GORDON

LEONARD LEOPOLD MACKALL

Writers on Servetus, almost without exception, seem to be pursued by some singular fatality leading to bibliographical inaccuracy —the most learned become illogical, and even professional bibliographers like van der Linde become careless for the occasion. Hence I hope that the following informal notes, as being based entirely on study of the rare original documents and accepting nothing on mere hearsay, will prove of value by correcting and supplementing various statements still current.

—Leonard L. Mackall, *Servetus Notes,* 1919.

Preface

This volume had its origin in a paper entitled *The Life and Death of Michael Servetus* read before the Club of Odd Volumes in Boston on 20 October 1948. Mr. Herbert Reichner of New York later suggested that it be issued as a small monograph with a full bibliography of Servetus' writings and source material appended. The compilation of the bibliography and the census of known copies of the rarer works required a much longer time than was at first anticipated. Meanwhile Dr. Earl Morse Wilbur's detailed bibliography covering Servetus' position in the history of the Unitarian movement makes it unnecessary to include this phase of his life and influence in the present bibliography of source material.* The bibliography has been completed with the assistance of Miss MADELINE E. STANTON, Librarian of Historical Collections in the Yale Medical Library.

The manuscript of the paper has been scrutinized by three eminent Servetus scholars: Professor Roland H. Bainton of Yale University, Dr. W. W. Francis of the Osler Library at McGill University, and Professor Charles D. O'Malley of Stanford University. Their queries and criticisms have resulted in greater accuracy and a more judicious view of the life and times of Servetus, and I am impelled to quote from letters from the first two because their feelings and reactions are those which almost inevitably assail anyone who studies the vast literature of the Reformation. "My horror for Calvin," writes Professor Bainton, "has come to be merged with a lament for the inhumanity of man to man. Calvin instigated the death of one man whom he considered a menace to man's security on earth and in heaven. Now we burn whole cities to preserve democracy." And from Dr. Francis: "I hate Calvin, but I don't think you should tar-and-feather him so unmercifully without quoting the modern

*Wilbur, E. M. *A bibliography of the pioneers of the Socinian-Unitarian movement in modern Christianity in Italy, Switzerland, Germany, Holland.* (Sussidi Eruditi 1.) Rome, Edizioni di Storia e Letteratura, 1950. 80 pp.

8   PREFACE

Genevans' inscription on their *Monument expiatoire*.* To paraphrase
Praed's 'Vicar,' our fathers were a long time learning

'That if a man's belief is bad,
It will not be improved by burning.'

You drive a car and have been known to fly. Nowadays we burn
more people than the old heretic and witch hunters ever did. Moreover they did it in the name of God to save souls; we do it in the
name of Progress to save minutes."

To Mr. O'Malley I am particularly indebted for all the quotations
I have used from the writings of Servetus. These appear in his book,
*Michael Servetus: A translation of his geographical, medical and astro-
logical writings with introductions and notes,* which was published in
October for the American Philosophical Society by Lloyd-Luke,
Ltd. of London in commemoration of the four hundredth anniver-
sary of Servetus' death.

Publication of the book has been made financially possible through
a generous gift from the Burndy Library, Norwalk, Connecticut,
and warm appreciation for this friendly gesture is hereby expressed.

Finally I must take this opportunity to express my thanks to
Mr. Reichner for his lively interest and co-operation, and for his
usual insistence on perfection in all that he undertakes to publish.

J.F.F.

*Department of the History of Medicine
Yale University
October 1953*

*Fils respectueux et reconnaissants de Calvin, notre grand réformateur, mais condamnant
une erreur qui fut celle de son siècle et fermement attachés à la liberté de conscience selon
les vrais principes de la réformation et de l'évangile nous avons élevé ce monument expiatoire
le XXVII octobre MCMIII.

Table of Contents

List of Illustrations

Short-title List of Writings of Servetus

Key to Library Abbreviations

ABERDEEN. University Library
AIX-EN-PROVENCE. Bibliothèque Méjanes
AMSTERDAM. Bibliotheek der Universiteit
AUGSBURG. Staats- und Stadtbibliothek
BASEL. Universitäts-Bibliothek
BERLIN. Öffentliche Wissenschaftliche Bibliothek (formerly Preussische
  Staatsbibliothek)
BERN. Stadt- und Hochschul-Bibliothek
BONN. Universitäts-Bibliothek
BORDEAUX. 1. Bibliothèque de la Ville
  2. Bibliothèque Universitaire
BRUSSELS. Bibliothèque Royale de Belgique
BUDAPEST. 1. Fövarosi Szabó Ervin Könyvtár (Public Library)
  2. Bibliotheca Universitatis
CAMBRIDGE, Eng. 1. King's College Library
  2. St. John's College Library
  3. Trinity College Library
  4. University Library
CLUJ [Kolozsvár, Klausenburg]. Unitarian College
COPENHAGEN. 1. Det Kongelige Bibliotek
  2. Universitetsbiblioteket
CRACOW. Biblioteka Jagiellonska
DRESDEN. Sächsische Landesbibliothek
DUBLIN. Trinity College Library
DURHAM. University Library
EDINBURGH. 1. National Library of Scotland (formerly the Advocates'
  Library)
  2. University Library
ERLANGEN. Universitätsbibliothek
FLORENCE. Biblioteca Nazionale Centrale
FRANKFURT am Main. Stadt- und Universitätsbibliothek
FREIBURG im Breisgau. Universitätsbibliothek
GENEVA. Bibliothèque Publique et Universitaire
GHENT [Gand]. Bibliotheek der Universiteit
GLASGOW. University Library
GÖTTINGEN. Niedersächsische Staats- und Universitäts-Bibliothek
GRENOBLE. Bibliothèque de Grenoble
THE HAGUE. Koninklijke Bibliotheek

HALLE (Saale). Universitäts- und Landesbibliothek Sachsen-Anhalt
HEIDELBERG. Universitäts-Bibliothek
JENA. Universitäts-Bibliothek
LEIDEN. Bibliotheek der Rijksuniversiteit
LEIPZIG. Universitäts-Bibliothek
LISBON. Biblioteca Nacional
LONDON. 1. British Museum
   2. Dr. Williams's Library
   3. Medical Society of London
   4. Royal College of Obstetricians and Gynaecologists
   5. Royal College of Physicians
   6. Royal College of Surgeons
   7. Wellcome Historical Medical Library
LYONS. Bibliothèque du Musée de Tissus
MADRID. Biblioteca Nacional
MANCHESTER. 1. John Rylands Library
     2. Unitarian College Library
MARBURG. Universitäts-Bibliothek
MILAN. Biblioteca Nazionale
MONTPELLIER. Bibliothèque de la Faculté de Médecine
MUNICH. 1. Bayerische Staatsbibliothek
   2. Universitäts-Bibliothek
NAPLES. Biblioteca Nazionale
OSLO. Universitetsbiblioteket
OXFORD. 1. Bodleian Library
   2. Christ Church Library
   3. Manchester College Library
   4. Wadham College Library
PARIS. 1. Académie de Médecine
   2. Bibliothèque de l'Arsenal
   3. Bibliothèque Mazarine
   4. Bibliothèque Nationale
   5. Bibliothèque de l'Université à la Sorbonne
   6. Université de Paris, Faculté de Médecine
   7. Université de Paris, Bibliothèque Sainte-Geneviève
   8. Société de l'Histoire du Protestantisme Français
PARMA. Biblioteca Palatina
PAVIA. Biblioteca Universitaria
ROME. 1. Biblioteca Nazionale Centrale
   2. Biblioteca Apostolica Vaticana
STOCKHOLM. Kungl. Biblioteket
STRASBOURG. Bibliothèque Nationale et Universitaire
STUTTGART. Württembergische Landesbibliothek

TURIN. Biblioteca Nazionale
TÜBINGEN. Universitäts-Bibliothek
UPSALA. 1. Universitetsbiblioteket
    2. Universitetsbiblioteket, Erik Waller Collection
UTRECHT. Bibliotheek der Rijksuniversiteit
VENICE. Biblioteca Nazionale di S. Marco
VIENNA. 1. Österreichische Nationalbibliothek
    2. Universitätsbibliothek
WARSAW. Universitätsbibliothek
WOLFENBÜTTEL. Stadtbibliothek
ZÜRICH. Zentralbibliothek

NORTH AMERICAN LIBRARIES

CaMM-Os	Osler Library, McGill University, Montreal, Canada
CaTAM	Academy of Medicine Library, Toronto, Canada.
CSt-L	Stanford University, Lane Medical Library at San Francisco, California
CBPac	Pacific Unitarian School (now Starr King School) for the Ministry, Berkeley, California
CSmH	Henry E. Huntington Library, San Marino, California
CtY-M	Yale Medical Library, New Haven, Connecticut
Dibner	The Burndy Library, Norwalk, Connecticut
DLC	Library of Congress, Washington, District of Columbia
DSG	Armed Forces Medical Library, Washington, District of Columbia
Humberd	Dr. Charles D. Humberd, Barnard, Missouri
ICN	Newberry Library, Chicago, Illinois
IEN-M	Northwestern University Medical School, Chicago, Illinois
ICU	University of Chicago Library, Chicago, Illinois
MBM	Boston Medical Library, Boston, Massachusetts
MH	Harvard University Library, Cambridge, Massachusetts
MdBJ-W	Johns Hopkins University, William H. Welch Medical Library, Baltimore, Maryland
MdBM	Medical & Chirurgical Faculty of the State of Maryland, Baltimore, Maryland
MnU	University of Minnesota Library, Minneapolis, Minnesota
MoSW-M	Washington University, Medical School Library, St. Louis, Missouri
NIC	Cornell University Library, Ithaca, New York
NN	New York Public Library, New York, New York
NNH	Library of the Hispanic Society, New York, New York

NNNAM	New York Academy of Medicine Library, New York, New York
NNP	Pierpont Morgan Library, New York, New York
NNC	Columbia University Library, New York, New York
NNUT	Union Theological Seminary Library, New York, New York
NjP	Princeton University Library, Princeton, New Jersey
O'Malley	Prof. Charles D. O'Malley, Stanford University, California
PPCP	Library of the College of Physicians, Philadelphia, Pennsylvania
RPB	Brown University Library, Providence, Rhode Island
RPJCB	John Carter Brown Library, Providence, Rhode Island
Trent	The late Dr. Josiah C. Trent, Durham, North Carolina

DE TRINI-
TATIS ERRORIBVS
LIBRI SEPTEM.

Per Michaelem Serueto, alias
Reues ab Aragonia
Hispanum.

Anno M. D. XXXI.

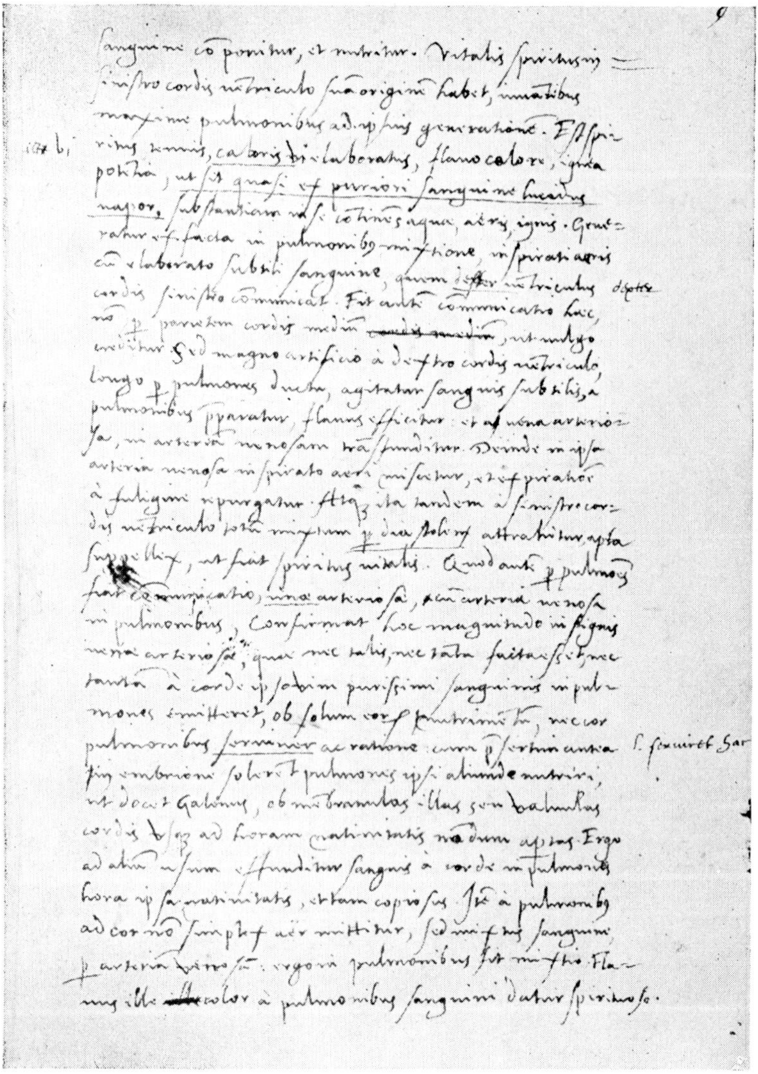

Fig. 2. A page from a manuscript written about 1546 containing the circulation passage. (Courtesy of the Bibliothèque Nationale, Paris). [See page 40].

Part I.

MICHAEL SERVETUS: HUMANIST
AND MARTYR

Chapter I

BACKGROUNDS: GALEN AND VESALIUS

GOOD BIOGRAPHY portrays a subject in the setting of his time and in relation to the spiritual forces which shaped his thought and destiny. In the case of Michael Servetus, the task is a challenging one for in him, a man of wealth and family, we find a free-thinking heretic, a polyhistor who took all knowledge for his province, including medicine, jurisprudence, physics, mathematics, geography, and theology. Born near Catalonia, Servetus, independent and fearless, inveighed against the outmoded dogmas of his time both in medicine and in theology. He early incurred the wrath of the theologians and to avoid the dragnet of the Spanish and French Inquisitors he was obliged to live in hiding under an assumed name for nearly twenty-five years; and he finally came to be sought even more fiercely by the archinquisitor, John Calvin, at whose hands he lost the fight for the privilege freely to speak his mind and was mercilessly burned at the stake on 27 October 1553.

From the perspective of four centuries it is clear that this freedom-loving man was resisting forces that came ultimately to overturn Western Europe—forces that still threaten civilization as we know it. For Servetus was one of that gallant band who endured martyrdom in order to proclaim the dignity of man and the freedom of the human spirit. But I propose to write of him not primarily as a symbol of man's long struggle for liberty, but rather because of his peculiar position in the history of physiological thought. To understand the nature of his contribution we must pause for a moment to consider the work of his most important predecessor in physiology, the Greek physician Galen who, although the founder of experimental physiology as the subject is now recognized, nevertheless impeded medical progress for some fifteen hundred years.

GALEN

Galen, private physician to the Emperor Marcus Aurelius, was born at Pergamum in Asia Minor and came to Rome in the year

164 when the Empire was at the zenith of its power—when the
legions of the Emperor held undisputed sway from Loch Lomond
to the Tigris and Euphrates. It was a period when Greek culture was
in its ascendance at Rome and Marcus Aurelius was writing his
Meditations in the Greek tongue. Galen as a passionate Hellenist
found his way immediately to the imperial court and with the
Emperor's patronage and sympathy he quickly became the most
influential physician in the Roman world.

Through his appointment as chief physician to the gladiators, first
at Pergamum and later at Rome, Galen had had opportunity to study
human physiology and particularly human neurophysiology at close
range, for gladiators and charioteers were in the habit of dislocating
their necks much as do our young men in modern football stadiums.
He had observed that some gladiators with dislocated necks died
instantly while others, paralyzed from the neck down, went on
breathing with their diaphragms, and being an experimentalist of
the highest order he was immediately curious to know how this
was to be explained. He resolved to find the answer in animals by
means of experiment.

Accordingly, Galen obtained a litter of newborn pigs, using the
young animals because it was easier to expose their spinal cords and
perhaps also because they did not squeal as lustily as older pigs. He
found when the spinal cord was cut halfway through on one side
that all the muscles below the cut on that side became paralyzed;
when the spinal cord was severed completely at the level of the third
cervical vertebra or above, the animal stopped breathing and died
instantly. When, however, the spinal cord was severed between the
seventh and eighth cervical vertebrae, the animal became paralyzed
and insentient from the neck down but went on breathing with its
diaphragm. On further dissection Galen found that the phrenic nerve
which controlled the diaphragm took origin from the mid-cervical
levels III, IV, and V and that when this nerve remained intact above
the level of transection, respiratory movements were still possible.
He thus provided a clear, scientific explanation of why the gladiators
with low cervical dislocations lived while those with high dislocations died; and he incidentally gave a masterful description of dia-
phragmatic as opposed to thoracic breathing.[1]

There was much else to Galen's credit in the way of experimentation; but when he approached the sphere of the vascular system his keen, intuitive sense largely forsook him. He had seen spurting arteries and had no doubt seen many a gladiator bleed to death. He was familiar with the dark color of venous blood since blood-letting was one of his oft-used therapeutic measures; but when he came to interpret these facts, he went badly astray.[2]

Ingested food, according to Galen's scheme, passed from the stomach and intestines to the liver where it was elaborated into blood. From the liver the blood so concocted ebbed and flowed backward and forward in the veins, thus to nourish the tissues. The red blood of the arteries which had been vitalized by passage into the lungs also ebbed and flowed, bringing vital spirits from the heart to the tissues. The venous blood on the right side of the heart had likewise to be refreshed and mixed with the vital spirits in the blood of the left side of the heart. What could be more simple? The vital spirits seeped through invisible pores in the cardiac septum. The system was complete, everything was now explained, and the invisible pores in the cardiac septum became official canon, not only of medicine but of the Church itself for nearly a millenium and a half; for Galen had taught that the body was the instrument of the soul—reasoning which coincided with Christian dogma and won for all his theories the approval of the Church. Indeed, his authority became so great that anyone who preached contrary doctrine was branded heretical both by Church and State.

Galen's influence was extended through his voluminous writings.

[1] Galen's experimental studies on the brain and spinal cord are scattered through many of his writings, e.g., *De usu partium*, *De motu musculorum*, and *De anatomicis administrationibus*. The best account of his experiments on the spinal cord is to be found in the last work (*Opera omnia*, Kühn ed., vol. 2, pp. 677–690). A useful French translation of the *De anat. admin.* was made by Jacques Dalechamps and published at Lyons in 1572. The most valuable modern study is that of J. S. Prendergast, "The background of Galen's life and activities, and its influence on his achievements" (*Proc. Roy. Soc. Med.*, 1930, *23*, 1131–1148). See also A. Souques' "Les connaissances neurologiques de Galien (aperçu critique)," (*Revue neurol.*, 1933, *1*, 297–340).

[2] Much has been written about Galen's views on the vascular system. The standard work and the most all-embracing is John C. Dalton's *Doctrines of the circulation. A history of physiological opinion and discovery, in regard to the circulation of the blood* (Philadelphia, Henry C. Lea's Son & Co., 1884. 296 pp.). The most searching recent analysis is that of J. S. Prendergast, "Galen's view of the vascular system in relation to that of Harvey" (*Proc. Roy. Soc. Med.*, 1928, *21*, 1839–1847). See also Charles Singer's *The discovery of the circulation of the blood* (London, G. Bell, 1922. x, 80 pp.).

His codices were copied and recopied by the scribes of the Dark
Ages and one hundred and twenty of his books have come down to
us, many of them garbled and imperfect but others bearing the un-
mistakable stamp of the master hand.[3] His *De usu partium* is probably the most remarkable from the physiological standpoint. The
fact that Galen's writings were adopted as official canon by the
Church, although not widely appreciated, helps in part to explain
why the Church reacted so violently both to Servetus and to his
fiery contemporary, Andreas Vesalius, who likewise concerned himself with the problem of the vascular system.

ANDREAS VESALIUS

On the last day of the year 1514 there was born at Brussels in
Belgium a man who was destined to shatter Galenical tradition.
This was Andreas Vesalius who not only founded human anatomy
as a modern science but re-established the experimental method and
inspired men to throw off the restrictions of theological dogma and
to think once again for themselves. The story of his phenomenal
career has often been told and need not be repeated in detail. He
had received his early training at Louvain, first in the Collegium
Trilingue and later at the University,[4] whence in 1533 he proceeded
to Paris where he became prosector in the laboratory of Guinterius[5]
whose attention he immediately attracted. Servetus in his turn was
to do the same a short time later, and Guinterius mentions both by
name in the preface of a new edition of his *Institutiones anatomicae*
which he brought out in 1539.[6]

[3] See Galen's *De libris propriis* and *De ordine librorum* (Kühn ed., *19*, 8–61).
[4] Fulton, J. F. "André Vésale, fondateur de l'anatomie moderne." *Revue des Questions Scien-
tifiques*, 20 April 1952, *13*, 161–170. See Chanoine Henry de Vocht's *History of the foundation and the rise of the Collegium Trilingue Lovaniense 1517–1550* (Louvain, Librairie Universitaire, 1951. xii, 662 pp.; 1953. viii, 694 pp.).
[5] Streeter, E. C. "Vesalius at Paris." *Yale J. Biol. Med.*, 1943, *16*, 121–128.
[6] Vesalius was mentioned alone in the first edition of August 1536. The reference in the ex-
panded preface of 1539 is as follows: "In this work (of revising this book in the light of
numerous dissections), not at all an easy one, I was helped, first by Andreas Vesalius—a
young man, by Hercules, most diligent in anatomy, and a professor of pure medicine for
whom one need not at all be sorry; only recently, in publishing this work of mine at Venice,
he furnished an excellent piece of [editorial] work. Next to him is Michael Villanovanus
[Servetus], who in a friendly manner assisted me in dissections—a man who would be an
ornament of any branch of letters, and who in Galenical doctrine is second to none." (From

By 1536 Vesalius had begun to question the Galenical texts and his independence of mind was disturbing to Guinterius, an ardent Galenist, and also to his Paris contemporary, Jacobus Sylvius, for whom Vesalius had also dissected. It was therefore perhaps fortunate that just before he would have presented himself for his medical degree Vesalius found it necessary to join his father, Court Pharmacist to the Emperor Charles V, on his march against the French, for almost certainly the degree would not have been granted.[5]

We next hear of Vesalius on 5 December 1537 when he was given an academic appointment to the faculty of the University of Padua, the chief responsibilities of which were to conduct anatomies for the benefit of the students and the public. He was not, as is sometimes said, made a professor of surgery at Padua in the modern sense, but being a member of the faculty gave him the right to teach.[7]

In the Spring of 1538 he issued with the aid of a Belgian contemporary, Jan van Calcar, his famous *Six Anatomical Tables;* and five years later, when he was twenty-eight years of age, he published his masterpiece, *De humani corporis fabrica,* a magnificent folio of nearly seven hundred pages. Here for the first time we find the structure of the human body systematically delineated and the more glaring Galenical errors put right, but Vesalius did not emancipate himself from Galen's teachings with regard to the vascular system. He did, however—and this is highly significant—express scepticism about the pores in the cardiac septum. Thus in the first edition of the *Fabrica*[8] he writes:

The fleshy processes are best discerned at the edge of the ventricles, or at their lower seat; I shall show that they contribute to the strength of the fibres which they contain, when in the second chapter after this I consider the nature of the membranes of the heart. Therefore the septum of the ventricles, as I said, formed from the thickest substance of the heart, abounds in pits impressed into both sides of it; for this reason the surface

Harvey Cushing's *Bio-bibliography of Andreas Vesalius*. New York, Schuman's, 1943. xxxviii, 229 pp. [p. xxvi])

[7] See Ivins in *Three Vesalian essays to accompany the 'Icones Anatomicae' of 1934,* by S. W. Lambert, W. Wiegand, and W. M. Ivins, Jr. New York, The Macmillan Co., 1952. xi, 128 pp. [pp. 101–107]

[8] *De humani corporis fabrica libri septem*. Basel, 1543, p. 589. I am indebted to Prof. O'Malley and Mr. Leon Nemoy for assistance in making this rendering.

which faces the ventricle is uneven. None of these pits (at least insofar as may be observed) penetrates from the right ventricle into the left, so that we are compelled to wonder at the industry of the Creator of all things by which the blood sweats from the right ventricle into the left through invisible passages.

The passage is changed in the second edition[9] to read:

And though these pits (*foveae*) are most conspicuous, none of them, as far as one can make out with one's eyes, passes from the right ventricle into the left through the septum of these ventricles. And I have not found even the most hidden passageways by which the septum of the ventricles could be penetrated, though they are mentioned by the professors of anatomy who are definitely convinced that the blood is taken over from the right into the left ventricle. As I shall demonstrate more fully later, I am therefore very much in doubt about the function of the heart in this particular part.

Singer[10] gives a further significant passage from the second edition of the *Fabrica* (page 734, lines 36 *et seq.*):

In considering the structure of the heart and the use of its parts, I have brought my words for the most part into agreement with the teachings of Galen: not because I thought that these were on every point in harmony with the truth, but because, in referring now and again to a new use and purpose for the parts, I still distrust myself. Not long ago I would not have dared to turn aside even a nail's breadth from the opinion of Galen, the prince of physicians. . . . But the septum of the heart is as thick, dense, and compact as the rest of the heart. I do not, therefore, know . . . in what way even the smallest particle can be transferred from the right to the left ventricle through the substance of that septum. . . . When these and other facts are considered, many points concerning the arteries come forward about which doubts may reasonably arise. We may note too that almost no vein goes to ventricle, intestines, or spleen without an accompanying artery, and likewise the portal vein has an accompanying artery almost throughout its course.

Thus Vesalius failed to make the logical deduction, though in the second edition he was much more sceptical about the pores than in 1543. Neither in the first nor in the second edition does he suggest the possibility of the passage of blood from the right to the left side

---

[9] *De humani corporis fabrica,* 2nd edition, Basel, 1555, p. 734.
[10] See reference in footnote 2 [pp. 27–28].

of the heart through the lungs. It remained for Michael Servetus to describe the pulmonary circulation.

Chapter II

THE CAREER OF MICHAEL SERVETUS

HAD ONE visited the town of Geneva on 27 October 1553, one would have been witness of that tragic scene which Osler[11] described so poignantly and dramatically:

. . . Shortly after twelve o'clock, a procession started from the town-hall of Geneva—the chief magistrates of the city, the clergy in their robes, the Lieutenant Criminel and other officers on horseback, a guard of mounted archers, the citizens, with a motley crowd of followers, and in their midst, with arms bound, in shabby, dirty clothes, walked a man of middle age, whose intellectual face bore the marks of long suffering. Passing along the rue St. Antoine through the gate of the same name, the cortège took its way towards the Golgotha of the city. Once outside the walls, a superb sight broke on their view: in the distance the blue waters and enchanting shores of the Lake of Geneva, to the west and north the immense amphitheatre of the Jura, with its snow-capped mountains, and to the south and west the lovely valley of the Rhone; but we may well think that few eyes were turned away from the central figure of that sad procession. By his side, in earnest entreaty, walked the aged pastor, Farel, who had devoted a long and useful life to the service of his fellow citizens. Mounting the hill, the field of Champel was reached, and here on a slight eminence was the fateful stake, with the dangling chains and heaping bundles of faggots. At this sight the poor victim prostrated himself on the ground in prayer. In reply to the exhortation of the clergyman for a specific confession of faith, there was the cry, 'Misericordia, misericordia! Jesu, thou Son of the eternal God, have compassion upon me!' Bound to the stake by the iron chain, with a chaplet of straw and green twigs covered with sulphur on his head, with his long dark face, it is said that he looked like the Christ in whose name he was bound. Around his waist were tied a large bundle of manuscript and a thick octavo printed book. The torch was applied, and as the flames spread to the straw and sulphur and flashed in his eyes, there was a piercing cry

[11] Osler, Wm. *Michael Servetus*. London, Oxford University Press, 1909. 35 pp. Also: *Johns Hopk. Hosp. Bull.*, 1910, *21*, 1–11. And in German: *Deutsche Revue*, 1909, *4*, 328–347. And in *Selected writings*, Oxford University Press, 1951, 100–125.

that struck terror into the hearts of the bystanders. The faggots were green, the burning was slow, and it was long before in a last agony he cried again, 'Jesu, thou Son of the eternal God, have mercy upon me!' Thus died, in his forty-fourth year, Michael Servetus Villanovanus, physician, physiologist, and heretic. Strange, is it not, that could he have cried, 'Jesu, thou Eternal Son of God!' even at this last moment, the chains would have been unwound, the chaplet removed, and the faggots scattered; but he remained faithful unto death to what he believed was the *Truth* as revealed in the Bible.

Born in 1511, it is thought at Tudela in Navarre, and reared in the hamlet of Villanueva de Sigena near Saragossa, Michael Servetus, the precocious scion of a well-to-do family, probably of Catalan origin, received his early education, reputedly first at the local College of Huesca and later at the University of Saragossa. When in his middle teens, his father sent him to the University of Toulouse to prepare for the law. But young Servetus had little taste for the law and while he did creditably at the University he soon found himself studying the scriptural texts which had only recently become available to scholars, perhaps from the pages of Cardinal Ximénes' *Complutensian Polyglot* which had been issued from the famous press at Alcalá de Henares near Madrid a few years earlier and first circulated in 1522.[12] While at Toulouse or possibly earlier, Servetus became the protégé of an influential and broadminded scholar, a Franciscan monk named Juan de Quintana, Court preacher to Emperor Charles V. The Emperor was to be crowned at Bologna in February 1530, and in the autumn of 1529 Quintana went there to prepare for the event, taking Servetus with him. Cornelius Agrippa related that "from every window in proud Bologna costly tapestries were hung forth. On every wall golden and silver gewgaws reflected the cheery radiance of the Italian sun. The very streets and arcades—the mighty arcades of Bologna . . . were carpeted with fresh flowers. Wine ran in the fountains from eagles' beaks and

---

[12] The *Complutensian Polyglot,* the earliest complete Polyglot Bible, was begun in 1502 by the great Spanish cardinal, Francisco Ximénes de Cisneros, assisted by a group of able scholars led by López de Zuñiga. The text of the Old Testament was issued in Hebrew and Latin Vulgate, Septuagint, and Chaldee, while the New Testament was issued in Greek and Latin. There were six folio volumes ranging in date from 1514 to 1517, but the huge undertaking did not receive papal sanction until March 1520, approval having been held up by Erasmus' Greek Testament, and the book was not actually circulated until 1522.

lions' gaping throats. Every nation from Britain in the West to the
isles of the Levant sent high dignitaries of Church and State, princes
and peers, cardinals and canons, in robes and badges of every imag-
ined description, to swell the pomp and multiply the parapher-
nalia."[13]

These elaborate preparations were anathema to the impressionable
Servetus, and the peak of his disgust came when he saw Pope
Clement VII carried through the streets on the papal sedia. Twenty
years later he recalled the scene with burning indignation:[14]

He dares not touch his feet to the earth, lest his holiness be defiled. He
has himself borne upon the shoulders of men, and adored as a God upon
earth. Since the foundation of the world no one has ever dared try any-
thing more wicked. With these very eyes we saw him carried with pomp
on the necks of princes, making threatening crosses with his hand, and
adored in the open squares by the whole people on bended knee; to such
a degree that those that were able to kiss his feet or his shoes deemed
themselves happy beyond others, said that they had got the greatest in-
dulgences, and that for this the punishments of hell had been remitted for
many years. O beast of beasts most wicked, harlot most shameless.

From now on the die was cast, and for the rest of his life Servetus
played the part of a lonely and zealous reformer; but so vehement
were his denunciations that he won few followers among either
Protestants or Catholics. His attempt to communicate with Erasmus
failed. Oecolampadius, the leader of the Swiss Reformation who
dwelt at Basel, had Servetus as a guest in his house for a long time
and tried to reason with him, but to no avail. Since he found no
sympathy for his views, Servetus set them down in a book entitled
De Trinitatis erroribus libri septem,[15] published without imprint by
the well-known printer, Johann Setzer of Hagenau in Alsace (some
fifteen miles north of Strasbourg). At the age of nineteen Servetus
had little thought of the personal danger to which he was exposing
himself in issuing this heretical piece and he naively placed his name
on the title: *per Michaelem Serveto, alias Reves ab Aragonia Hispanum.*

[13] Gordon, Alexander. "The personality of Michael Servetus." In his: *Addresses biographical and historical.* London, The Lindsey Press, 1922. 350 pp. [pp. 16–17]
[14] Wilbur, Earl Morse. *A history of Unitarianism, socinianism and its antecedents.* Cambridge, Harvard University Press, 1946. xiii, 617 pp. [p. 55]
[15] Bibliographical details concerning this and the other writings of Servetus are given in Part II.

I shall not attempt to describe the contents of the book for it is concerned with subtleties of theological disputation. Suffice it to say that it shocked Catholic and reformer alike, but now stands as a great cornerstone in the history of the Unitarian movement.[16]

The outburst against the young heretic became so intense that in 1532 he published a formal retraction which appeared at the beginning of a second tract known as the *Dialogorum de Trinitate, libri duo*. The retraction has been rendered thus:[16]

TO THE READER, GREETINGS

All that I have lately written, in seven Books, against the received view as to the Trinity, honest reader, I now retract; not because it is untrue, but because it is incomplete, and written as though by a child for children. Yet I pray you to keep such of it as might help you to an understanding of what is to be said here. Moreover, that such a barbarous, confused, and incorrect book appeared as my former one was, must be ascribed to my own lack of experience, and to the printer's carelessness. Nor would I have any Christian offended thereby, since God is wont sometimes to make his own wisdom known through the foolish instruments of the world. I beg you, therefore, to pay attention to the matter itself; for if you give heed to this, my halting words will not stand in your way. Fare you well.

This, however, did not satisfy his critics, and Servetus was obliged to go thereafter into hiding and adopt for his surname that of the village where he had been reared.

Before dealing with the later phases of his life, let me indulge in a bibliographical digression. The *De Trinitatis erroribus* is a rare book, the *Dialogi de Trinitate* of 1532 even rarer; indeed, in 1553 when Servetus was being tried for heresy, Calvin was unable to find a copy of either tract in any library of Europe. Farel, who accompanied Servetus to the stake, later produced one from Vienna (Fig. 1). During the eighteenth century the book was so much sought after by the friends of Unitarianism that it was reprinted, page for page and virtually line for line, and to conceal the forgery even the typographical errors were perpetuated; but the eighteenth-century printer did not have double hyphens either for text or title-page, so

---

[16] *The two treatises of Servetus on the Trinity.* . . . Now first translated into English by Earl Morse Wilbur. Cambridge, Harvard University Press, 1932. See also note 14.

that the spurious edition can readily be distinguished from the original by a glance at the title. Sir William Osler, in his well-known essay on Servetus, was misled into giving the spurious title as the original. According to Mackall[17] the forgery was made about 1721 by the Reverend Georg Serpilius (1668–1723), a prominent clergyman and hymnologist of Regensburg. Quite apart from the heretical nature of Servetus' views, the book is remarkable for the extraordinary range of authors cited and also for the fact that he displays a considerable knowledge both of Greek and Hebrew which he must have learned at Toulouse before he was twenty.

Servetus so successfully concealed his identity that twenty-one years were to elapse before it was publicly discovered that Michael Servetus and Michael Villanovanus were one and the same person. Indeed his success in concealing himself has made it difficult to trace his movements between 1532 and 1535 when we know he was at Lyons working for the Trechsels, scholar-printers, engaged in bringing out an edition of Ptolemy's *Geography*. It is conceivable that he had begun his medical studies in Paris (Fig. 3) during this interval and that he went to Lyons in order to support himself. In any event, he was back in Paris toward the end of 1536 under the patronage of the great Lyons humanist, Symphorien Champier. Thus in November we find him rising to Champier's defence in a pamphlet addressed to Leonard Fuchs, the distinguished botanist (*In Leonardum Fuchsium apologia*. [Lyons] 1536). For the next year or two, under the stimulating guidance of Jean Fernel, Jacobus Sylvius, and Joannes Guinterius, Servetus pursued his medical studies, but it is not known where he received his medical degree.

Some idea of student life in France at that time is found in Sir Charles Sherrington's vivid biography of Jean Fernel, one of Servetus' teachers at Paris.[18] Thus:

Custom at that time began the day earlier than now. Gargantua and his tutor, we remember, started the day at four. Five o'clock seems to

[17] Mackall, L. L. "Servetus notes." In: *Contributions to medical and biological research, dedicated to Sir William Osler, in honour of his seventieth birthday, July 22, 1919, by his pupils and co-workers*. New York, Paul B. Hoeber, 1919. 2 vols. [Vol. 2, pp. 767–777]
[18] Sherrington, Sir Charles. *The endeavour of Jean Fernel, with a list of the editions of his writings*. Cambridge, Eng., University Press, 1946. x, 223 pp. [p. 60]

have been usual for commencing the University lecture day. 'We were up at 4, and, having said our prayer, went to 5 o'clock lecture, our huge books tucked under one arm, writing-case and candle-stick in our hands. Lectures lasted until 10. Then, after half-an-hour for correcting our notes, we went in to dinner. From one o'clock onward we attended lectures again, and at five o'clock got back to our lodgings, went through our notes and looked up references. Supper at 6 o'clock.' Thus Henri de Mesmes, a young student at Toulouse, describes his University day there, in the year 1545.

Servetus' career in Paris was brought to an end by an unfortunate incident, for in 1538 (old style March 1537) he was publicly condemned by the Parlement de Paris at the behest of the Paris Faculty for his lectures on judicial astrology, offered while he was carrying on his medical studies. Astrology at that time was stoutly rejected by the reactionary Faculty, but Servetus persisted and against the advice of the Dean published his *Apologetica disceptatio pro astrologia* (see pages 76–78) in which he attacked his colleagues and maintained, moreover, that wars and pests and all the affairs of men depended upon the heavens and upon the stars. Thus he says:

In company with certain friends I observed a similar event occurring on the twelfth of this month of February in the year 1538. With night falling, Mars was eclipsed by the moon near the star which is called king or lion-heart. Whence I predicted it would happen that in this year the hearts of the lions, that is the minds of the princes, would be aroused more greedily, to take up arms with Mars, and much would be laid waste by fire and sword, and the church would suffer much, certain princes would die and in addition plagues and other things, which God avert. But enough of these things.

The 18-page pamphlet, the rarest of all Servetus items,[19] was confiscated when Servetus was brought to trial.

At his trial Servetus made a brilliant defence with learned citations from Plato, Aristotle, Hippocrates, and Galen, and was acquitted of heresy by the Inquisition but ordered by the Faculty to abandon his lectures. In the meantime, he committed to the press of Simon de Colines of Paris a short but creditable treatise on the therapeutic value of the syrups, his only direct excursion into medi-

[19] Only two copies are known to have survived: in the Bibliothèque Nationale and the Library of the Sorbonne, Paris.

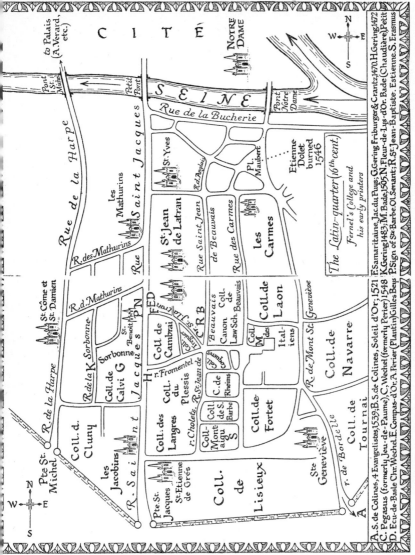

Fig. 3. The Latin Quarter of Paris at the time of Servetus' sojourn there. (From Sir Charles Sherrington's *The Endeavour of Jean Fernel*, 1946. Kindness of the Cambridge University Press).

A. S. de Colines, 1539. B. S. de Colines, Soleil d'Or; 1521 F. Samaritaine, Jac. du Puys; G. Gering Friburger & Crantz; 1470. H. Gering; 1472 C. Pegasus (formerly Jeu-de-Paume); C, Wechel (formerly Perier) 1548 K. Gering 1483; M. Bade, 1505. N. Fleur-de-1 ys-d'Or. Bade (Chaudière); Petit D. Ecu-de-Basle Chr. Wechel. E. Compas-d'Or: A. Perier (Plantin) Gilles Beys P. Sign of Ste Barbe. O. Senant; R. St Jean-Baptiste. Estienne. S. Erasmus

cal writing.[20] The *Syrups,* although a medical treatise, is clearly not
the work of a seasoned clinical observer, for at the time it was
written Servetus had probably not yet formally entered upon his
medical studies but he had served for a year or more in the entour-
age of Champier who was engaged in medical practice. The book
exhibits little originality but indicates Servetus' thorough mastery
of the Galenical and other ancient writings in the field of digestion.
He sets forth in detail the theory of the first and second concoctions
whereby food is transformed in the stomach and intestines into
nutrient materials which are ultimately transformed in the liver
into blood. The various extracts of medicinal plants, referred to
broadly as syrups, are discussed in relation to their possible assistance
to the digestive processes in health and disease.

After leaving Paris, Servetus settled for a time at Avignon and
later at Charlieu. In both places he was engaged in general medical
practice. In 1541 Pierre Palmier, Archbishop of Vienne and Primate
of all France, invited Servetus to settle in Vienne. The Archbishop
apparently admired Servetus' independence of mind; but it would
seem that he softened the younger man's fanaticism, for in the 1541
edition of the Ptolemy dedicated to the Archbishop, Servetus removed the cynical remarks which he had used in reference to
Palestine not being a land of milk and honey, and he no longer took
issue with the claim that kings could cure the scrofula by royal
touch. The *Geography* showed a vast knowledge of general literature. Among the many passages which invite quotation, one about
Scotland is particularly interesting (omissions from the second edition are given in italics, additions in square brackets):[21]

Among Scots there are few differences of customs, *language or manners.*
Their temper is hasty, prone to revenge, and fierce. They are brave in
war, very patient under fasting, watching and cold, shapely in mien,
careless in dress. *Unfriendly in disposition, they look down on all other mortals.*
They are vain of their noble blood; even in the depth of poverty tracing
their pedigree to a line of kings. *They flatter themselves on their argumenta-
tive skill; in lying they delight, and do not study peace, like the English.* [The

---

[20] First appearing in 1537, the book was reprinted twice at Venice (1545 and 1548) and
thrice at Lyons (1546, 1547, and 1548)—see page 69 *et seq.*
[21] See Gordon (footnote 13), p. 29.

DEFENSIO ORTHODOXAE

fidei de ſacra Trinitate, côtra prodigio-
ſos errores Michaelis Serueti Hiſpani:
vbi oſtenditur hæreticos iureGladii co-
ercendos eſſe, & nominatim de homine
hoc tam impio iuſtè & meritò ſumptú
Geneuæ fuiſſe ſupplicium.

Per Iohannem Caluinum.

Oliua Roberti Stephani.

M. D. L I I I I.

Fig. 4. Title-page of Calvin's unrepenting defence of
himself. The Latin edition of 1554. [See page 36].

DECLARATION
POVR MAINTENIR LA
vraye foy que tiennent tous Chrestiens
de la Trinité des persones en vn seul Dieu.

PAR IEAN CALVIN.

Contre les erreurs detestables de Michel Ser-
uet Espaignol. Ou il est aussi monstré, qu'il
est licite de punir les heretiques : & qu'à
bon droict ce meschant a esté executé par iu-
stice en la ville de Geneue.

CHEZ IEAN CRESPIN
A GENEVE,

M. D. LIIII.

Fig. 5. Title-page of Calvin's unrepenting defence of
himself. The French edition appeared in the same year
as the Latin and is here reproduced through the courtesy of the New York Public Library. [See page 36].

northern parts of Scotland are tenanted by wild men, bearing the name of foresters; their speech and dress are as in Ireland; they wear a rug over a tunic of saffron dye, and go with bare shanks and a shaggy kind of footwear; they live on game and fish, though with plenty of cattle, milk and cheese; their weapons are bows and arrows, and broadswords; hunting is their chief pursuit; they have a provincial code, different from the civil law. The rest of the Scots are similar to the English in language and civilization. Almost throughout the island] the use of coal for firing is so common that beggars meeting charitable persons ask for coal.

After the Ptolemy, Servetus' major project lay in the editing of a new edition of Pagnino's translation of the Bible. Santes Pagninus (1470–1531), an erudite Dominican monk from Lucca, had devoted twenty-five years to translating the Bible into Latin and had first published it at Lyons in 1527–28. At the time of his death Pagnino left a large volume of notes and marginal corrections in his personal copy. This Bible fell into the hands of the enterprising house of the de la Portes at Lyons who promptly invited Servetus to take charge of the revision. This he did with his usual promptness, and within a year the new and sumptuously printed Pagnini Bible was off the press. Servetus contributed a noteworthy preface[22] in which he urged Biblical scholars to learn Hebrew and to familiarize themselves with early Hebrew history before undertaking to interpret the prophets. Some of Servetus' marginalia were seized upon as being heretical and the book was placed on the Louvain Index and also upon that of Madrid; but Servetus was not brought to trial. Wilbur believes that the chief importance of the undertaking from Servetus' standpoint lay in the fact that it rekindled his interest in questions of religion and that it caused him once again to begin brooding over his old plan to restore Christianity to the original scriptural simplicity and purity.

Servetus had twelve happy years quietly practising medicine near Lyons and serving as editorial assistant to the local printers including Frellon, Trechsel,[23] and possibly also to the unfortunate Étienne Dolet who was burned at the stake by the infamous Lyons In-

---

[2] Wilbur, op. cit. (note 14), p. 129.

[3] See Baudrier, J. "Michel Servet: ses relations avec les libraires et les imprimeurs Lyonnais." In: Mélanges offerts à M. Émile Picot . . . par ses amis et ses élèves. Paris, E. Rahir, 1913. 2 vols. Vol. I, pp. 41–56]

quisitor, Mathiew D'Ory. Dolet had met this fate in August 1546, so Servetus must have been aware of the tremendous hazard he faced in issuing a book on which he had worked for many years in the fond hope that it would restore Christianity to the simple state in which he believed it to have been conceived. But in this year he had begun a correspondence with Calvin, who was now the acknowledged leader of the Protestant Reformation, and had unwisely submitted part of his manuscript to him. Servetus even offered to go to Geneva, but Calvin wrote to one of his correspondents (Farel): "I will not pledge my faith to him, for did he come, had I any authority here, I should not suffer him to go away alive." Servetus persevered in his intention to issue the book; but finding no printer willing to risk the publication, he finally had his manuscript, entitled *Christianismi restitutio,* set up privately and anonymously at Vienne in 1553. Calvin received a copy immediately, and after due enquiry denounced Servetus to the Lyons Inquisitor.

The only account of Servetus' first trial, at Vienne, is that left us by the painstaking scholar, the abbé Antoine Gachet d'Artigny (1706–1778), who as Canon of the Cathedral at Vienne en Dauphiné had access to all the town and church records at Vienne. He states[24] that the Archbishop of Vienne (Pierre Palmier) decided he had sufficient evidence to justify bringing Servetus to trial for heresy. He accordingly summoned Mathiew D'Ory, the Inquisitor, and by April 4th Palmier and several other local ecclesiastics assembled at Château Roussillon to pass judgment. They produced as evidence Servetus' own annotated copy of the *Christianismi restitutio* and some twenty letters which he had addressed to Calvin. The charge of heresy was established beyond all question, and Servetus stood convicted on his own testimony. 'Michel Servet de Villeneufe au Royaume d'Aragon en Espagne' was forthwith apprehended along

[24] Artigny, Antoine Gachet d'. *Nouveaux mémoires d'histoire, de critique et de littérature.* Paris 1749–1756. 7 vols. In Vol. 2, pp. 55–154, Article XL carries the title "Mémoires pour servir à l'histoire de Michel Servet." The Osler Library possesses a copy of d'Artigny's *Mémoires* in which the following note is inserted: "A MS. note on the flyleaf of vol. 1, by the donor Mr. L. L. Mackall, 1914, states, 'Rev. Alex. Gordon, author of the article "Servetus" in the new Encycl. Brit. told me that these volumes are so rare that he has never heard of a set being sold. Vol. 7, 1756, is lacking, but it contains nothing on Servetus.'" See also Hemmeter J. C. "Michael Servetus. Discoverer of the pulmonary circulation. His life and work." *Janus* 1915, *20,* 331–360, 9 pl.

with Balthazar Arnoullet who had printed the *Restitutio*. His arrest was accomplished by the ruse of asking him to go to the Royal Palace of the Archbishop to treat some ailing prisoners. Servetus complied, stating that it was his duty as a physician to minister to the suffering; he was then told that he would remain confined to the Palace until the charges against him had been satisfactorily answered. His jailor, Antoine Bouin, had injunctions to watch him carefully since Servetus was surrounded in Vienne by many loyal friends and grateful patients who would no doubt attempt to secure his escape. At four o'clock on the morning of the 7th of April he appeared before Bouin cleverly disguised in night dress and night cap and asked for the key to the garden which Bouin promptly gave him; Servetus was thus able to get away with clothing concealed beneath his night dress. He placed his black velvet bonnet and dressing gown at the base of a tree, lept from the terrace of the garden to a roof below, and thence made off to the Roman bridge which spans the Rhone. Every effort was made to recapture him; the gates of the city were closed, but it was too late, for Servetus was at large and he had many friends along the route south who would give him asylum. With cold precision the infuriated Inquisitor continued his search and meanwhile prepared a brief of all the errors contained in the *Restitutio* which was read on June 17th and an effigy of Servetus burned along with five hundred copies of his book.

Some three months later Servetus arrived in Geneva on his way to Italy. Why he took the risk of being there on Sunday when attendance at church was obligatory will never be known. He was recognized, and Calvin promptly had him arrested on August 14th. Servetus spent the remaining days of his life in an atrocious dungeon with no light or heat, little food, and no sanitary facilities; but he was allowed to emerge on the days when his presence was needed at his barbaric trial which is one of the sorriest episodes in history, and surely one of the most farcical in man's struggle for his freedom.[25] All Geneva was divided into hostile camps. Servetus him

[25] Rilliet, Albert. *Relation du procès criminal intenté à Genève, en 1553, contre Michel Servet, redigée d'après les documents originaux.* Genève, 1844. (Reprinted from *Mémoires et Documents publiés par la Societé d'histoire et d'archéologie de Genève,* 1844, *3,* 1–125.) See also Willis,

self continued to be surprised that he was not received with open arms by the Swiss Protestants who, as he thought, were like himself struggling to overthrow the abuses of the Catholic Church. Finally, on October 27th, he was summoned to hear the verdict. There was no delay; the procession formed immediately and within a few hours Servetus was in his final agony, paying the supreme price for the privilege of worshiping God in accordance with his own lights.

Calvin had thus murdered his enemy, and there is nothing to suggest that he ever repented his crime. The next year he published a defence[26] in which further insults were heaped upon his former adversary in most vindictive and intemperate language (Figs. 4 and 5). One finds it difficult to be as forbearing as Osler who wrote of Calvin: "Let his one grievous fault be the shadow which throws into stronger relief the splendid outlines of a noble life"—charitable language to apply to a bigoted and merciless churchman.

Chapter III

THE DISCOVERY OF THE LESSER CIRCULATION

SERVETUS' celebrated description of the lesser circulation[27] of blood through the lungs is found in the fifth book of the *Christianismi restitutio* (Fig. 6) during a discussion on the nature of the Divine Spirit. His interest in the blood arose from his

Robert. *Servetus and Calvin. A study of an important epoch in the early history of the Reformation.* London, H. S. King & Co., 1877. xvi, 541 pp.

[26] Calvin, Jean. *Defensio orthodoxae fidei de sacra Trinitate, contra prodigiosos errores Michaelis Serveti Hispani: . . .* [Geneva], Oliva Robert Estienne, 1554. 261 pp. See Fig. 4. A French edition of this tract appeared the same year: *Declaration pour maintenir la vraye foy que tiennent tous Chrestiens de la Trinité des persones en un seul Dieu. Contre les erreurs detestables de Michel Servet Espaignol.* Geneve, chez Jean Crespin, 1544. 356 pp., 2 *ll.* See Fig. 5.

[27] The best accounts of Servetus' discovery are those of: Pierre Flourens, *Histoire de la découverte de la circulation du sang.* Paris, J. B. Baillière, 1854. viii, 216 pp.; Henri Tollin, *Die Entdeckung des Blutkreislaufs durch Michael Servet (1511–1553).* Jena, H. Dufft, 1876. 4 *ll.*, 81 pp.; John C. Dalton, 1884 (see note 2); John C. Hemmeter, 1915 (see note 24); Roland H. Bainton, "The smaller circulation: Servetus and Colombo." *Sudhoffs Arch. Gesch. Med.,* 1931, *34,* 371–374; J. J. Izquierdo, "A new and more correct version of the views of Servetus on the circulation of the blood." *Bull. Hist. Med.,* 1937, *5,* 914–932; Josep Trueta, "Michael Servetus and the discovery of the lesser circulation." *Yale J. Biol. Med.,* 1948, *21,* 1–15; R. H. Bainton, "Michael Servetus and the pulmonary transit of the blood." *Bull. Hist. Med.,* 1951, *25,* 1–7 (Garrison Lecture).

conviction that the soul of man dwelt in the blood stream; to understand the soul, therefore, one must study the origin and movement
of the blood itself. I give the historic passages describing the lesser
circulation in Professor C. D. O'Malley's excellent new rendering
from pages 168–172 of the original text. I have italicized two passages: the first describing the pulmonary circulation, the second that
in which Servetus states that the vital spirit is "transfused from the
left ventricle into the arteries of the whole body" (*a sinistro cordis
ventriculo, in arterias totius corporis deinde transfunditur*) which indicates
clearly, but does not actually prove, that Servetus may have had
some glimmering of the greater circulation. It is evident, however,
as Dr. O'Malley points out in a personal communication (31 December 1952), that Servetus was writing more as a theologian than
as a physiologist, and that he was more interested in the course
taken by the *spiritus* than in the path travelled by the blood itself;
the passage of blood through the lungs is cited only to illustrate this
point. The revealing introductory passages on pages 168–169 of the
original edition have not previously been translated (the numbers in
square brackets indicate the pages of the original text):

From a breath of air God there introduces the Divine Spirit into men
in whom the life of the inspired air was innate. Hence in Hebrew "spirit"
is represented in the same way as "breath." From the air God introduces
the Divine Spirit, introducing the air with the spirit itself and the spark
of the very deity which fills the air. The saying of Orpheus is true, that
the Divine Spirit is carried by the winds and enters through full inspiration, as Aristotle cites in his book *De anima*. [169] Ezekiel teaches that the
Divine Spirit contains a kind of elemental substance and, as God himself
teaches, something in the substance of the blood. I shall explain this
matter at greater length here so that you may thence understand that the
substance of the created Spirit of Christ is essentially joined to the very
substance of the Holy Spirit. I shall call the air 'spirit' because in the
sacred language there is no special name for air. Indeed, that fact indicates
that the divine breath is in the air which the Spirit of the Lord fills.

So that you, the reader, may have the whole doctrine of the Divine
Spirit and the spirit, I shall add here the divine philosophy which you
will easily understand if you have been trained in anatomy. It is said that
in us there is triple spirit from the substance of three higher elements,
natural, vital, and animal. Aphrodisaeus calls them three spirits. But they
are not three but once again of the single spirit (*spiritus*). The vital spirit

is that which is communicated through anastomoses from the arteries to the veins in which it is called the natural [spirit]. Therefore the first [i.e., natural spirit] is of the blood, and its seat is in the liver and in the veins of the body. The second is the vital spirit of which the seat is in the heart and in the arteries of the body. The third is in the animal spirit, a ray of light, as it were, of which the seat is in the brain and the nerves of the body. In all of these there resides the energy of the one spirit and of the light of God. The formation of man from the uterus teaches that the vital spirit is communicated from the heart to the liver. For an artery joined to a vein is transmitted through the umbilicus of the foetus, and in like manner afterward the artery and vein are always joined in us. The Divine Spirit of Adam was inspired from God into the heart before [it was communicated into] the liver, and from there was communicated to the liver. The Divine Spirit was truly drawn from the mouth and nostrils, but the inspiration extended to the heart. The heart is the first living thing, the source of heat in the middle of the body. From the liver it takes the liquid of life, a kind of material, and in return vivifies it, just as the liquid of water furnishes material for higher substances and by them, with the addition of light, is vivified so that [in turn] it may invigorate. The material of the Divine Spirit is from the blood of the liver by way of a remarkable elaboration [170] of which you will now hear. Hence it is said that the Divine Spirit is in the blood, and the Divine Spirit is itself the blood, or the sanguineous spirit. It is not said that the Divine Spirit is principally in the walls of the heart, or in the body of the brain or of the liver, but in the blood, as is taught by God himself in *Gen.* 9, *Levit.* 7, and *Deut.* 12 [Figs. 7 and 8].

In this matter there must first be understood the substantial generation of the vital spirit which is composed of a very subtle blood nourished by the inspired air. The vital spirit has its origin in the left ventricle of the heart, and the lungs assist greatly in its generation. It is a rarefied spirit, elaborated by the force of heat, reddish-yellow (*flavo*) in color and of fiery potency, so that it is a kind of clear vapor from very pure blood, containing in itself the substance of water, air, and fire. It is generated in the lungs from a mixture of inspired air with elaborated, subtle blood which the right ventricle of the heart communicates to the left. *However, this communication is made not through the middle wall of the heart, as is commonly believed, but by a very ingenious arrangement the subtle blood is urged forward by a long course through the lungs; it is elaborated by the lungs, becomes reddish-yellow and is poured from the pulmonary artery into the pulmonary vein. Then in the pulmonary vein it is mixed with inspired air and through expiration it is cleansed of its sooty vapors. Thus finally the whole mixture, suitably prepared for the production of the vital spirit, is drawn onward from the left ventricle of the heart by diastole.* [Italics mine. J.F.F.]

That the communication and elaboration are accomplished in this way through the lungs we are taught by the different conjunctions and the communication of the pulmonary artery with the pulmonary vein in the lungs. The notable size of the pulmonary artery confirms this; that is, it was not made of such sort or of such size, nor does it emit so great a force of pure blood from the heart itself into the lungs merely for their nourishment; nor would the heart be of such service to the lungs, since at an earlier stage, in the embryo, the lungs, as Galen teaches, are nourished from elsewhere because those little membranes or [171] valvules of the heart are not opened until the time of birth. Therefore that the blood is poured from the heart into the lungs at the very time of birth, and so copiously, is for another purpose. Likewise, not merely air, but air mixed with blood, is sent from the lungs to the heart through the pulmonary vein; therefore the mixture occurs in the lungs. The reddish-yellow color is given to the spirituous blood by the lungs; it is not from the heart.

In the left ventricle of the heart there is no place large enough for so great and copious a mixture, nor for that elaboration imbuing the reddish-yellow color. Finally, that middle wall, since it is lacking in vessels and mechanisms, is not suitable for that communication and elaboration, although something may possibly sweat through. By the same arrangement by which a transfusion of the blood from the portal vein to the vena cava occurs in the liver, also a transfusion of the spirit from the pulmonary artery to the pulmonary vein occurs in the lung. If anyone compares these things with those which Galen wrote in Books VI and VII, *De usu partium,* he will thoroughly understand a truth which was unknown to Galen.

And so that vital spirit is then transfused from the left ventricle of the heart into the arteries of the whole body so that that which is more rarefied seeks the higher regions where it is further elaborated, especially in the retiform plexus situated under the base of the brain, and approaching the special seat of the rational soul the animal spirit begins to be formed from the vital. [Italics mine. J.F.F.] Again it is more greatly rarefied by the fiery force of the mind, elaborated, and completed in the very slender vessels or hair-like [*capillaribus*] arteries which are situated in the choroid plexuses and contain the mind itself. These plexuses penetrate all the inmost parts of the brain, internally girdling the ventricles of the brain, and those vessels, enfolded and woven together as far as the origins of the nerves, serve to introduce in these last the faculties of sensation and of motion. Those vessels in a very remarkable way are woven together very finely, and even if they are called arteries, nevertheless they are the terminations of arteries [172] extending through the assistance of the meninges to the origin of the nerves. It is a new kind of vessels. For just as in the transfusion from the veins into the arteries there is a new kind of vessels in the lung, from vein and artery, so in the transfusion from the arteries into the nerves there is a new kind of vessels from the tunic of the artery in the meninx, since especially do the meninges preserve their tunics in the nerves. The sensibility of the nerves is not in their soft material, as in the brain. All nerves end in membranous filaments which have the most exquisite sensibility and to which for this reason the spirit is always sent. And from those little vessels of the meninges, or choroid plexuses, as from a source, the clear animal spirit is poured forth like a ray through the nerves into the eyes and other sense organs. By the same route, but in reverse, light images of things causing sensation coming from without are sent to the same source, penetrating inwardly, as it were, through the clear medium [i.e., spirit].[28]

This passage indicates that Servetus' anatomical knowledge was sound, for the account of the blood vessels of the lungs in relation to the heart is by far the most accurate that had yet appeared. How he could thus speak with such assurance concerning the actual circulation of the blood through the lungs from the right to the left side of the heart will probably ever remain a mystery, but it was no doubt based upon his anatomical dissections in Paris and his later studies while practising as a physician in Vienne and Lyons. Servetus had recorded his discovery of the pulmonary transit as early as 1546 for, as Mackall has emphasized, there is a manuscript of the *Restitutio* in the Bibliothèque Nationale containing the passage on the lesser circulation (Fig. 2) which had been written in or before that year.[29]

---

[28] In a personal communication of 28 December 1952 Professor O'Malley makes this illuminating comment on his English rendering: "There is difficulty over the translation of *anima* and *spiritus* which both mean 'spirit' although the former frequently means 'Divine spirit' and the latter a kind of 'world spirit,' yet the former is present in the latter. Bainton tried to get around this by using 'soul' for *anima* which, however, does not always work; and Wilbur tried 'divine essence' which I think was not too successful. The difficulty is one of distinction, and I am pretty sure that Servetus wasn't always quite sure. If theology had not interfered, he could have employed 'pneuma' for *spiritus,* which would have simplified matters somewhat, but of course we cannot use it without distortion of some of Servetus' views. Also that irritating word *flavus,* 'yellow' or 'reddish yellow.' Translators, including the most recent, Trueta, say that this must be translated as red, presumably because blood is red. Now it happens that there are several good adjectives in Latin which mean red or reddish. Why then didn't Servetus use one of them if he thought that arterial blood was red? In short, the translators don't translate but use words which they believe the situation calls for. But suppose Servetus was color-blind, is it not possible that the color he saw was *flavus*?" It might well be. J.F.F.

[29] Mackall, Leonard L. "A manuscript of the 'Christianismi restitutio' of Servetus, placing the discovery of the pulmonary circulation anterior [*sic*] to 1546." *Proc. R. Soc. Med.* (Hist. Sec.), 1924, *17*, 35–38. Alexander Gordon had earlier (1878) called attention to this MS.

As we have seen, Vesalius did not grasp the idea of the pulmonary circulation even when he issued the second edition of the *Fabrica* in 1555, and Servetus' description was to remain for many years between the covers of the three surviving copies of the *Christianismi restitutio*. The first widely circulated account of the pulmonary circulation occurs in the Spanish paraphrase of the *Fabrica* by Servetus' fellow Spaniard, Juan Valverde de Hamusco, published at Rome in 1556.[30] The Valverde preface is dated 1554, and in introducing the passage on the lesser circulation Valverde is careful to state that "nobody before me has ever said this." Josep Trueta, who has included a stimulating essay on Servetus in his book, *The Spirit of Catalonia*,[31] is of the opinion that Valverde must have known of Servetus' account of the circulation (his description follows that of Servetus very closely), but he dared not make public reference to a book or to an author so violently condemned both by the Inquisition and by Calvin. Dr. Trueta bases his conclusion principally on the fact that in Valverde's *De animi et corporis sanitate* published at Paris in 1552 there is no mention of the pulmonary circulation despite the fact that he considered the heart and vascular system at some length (pp. 119–125).

The question of priority is further complicated by the fact that Realdo Colombo, one of Vesalius' successors in the chair of anatomy at Padua, had described the pulmonary circulation in his lectures, and Valverde was one of his pupils. However, Colombo did not live to publish his volume on anatomy on which he had been at work for many years. The book was modelled after the *Fabrica* and in it Colombo indicates that he hoped to correct "the many errors of Vesalius." It appeared under the title *De re anatomica;*[32] but it was not published until 1559, a few months after the death of Colombo and three years after the appearance of Valverde's Spanish paraphrase of the *Fabrica*.[33] *De re anatomica* contains a description of the

[30] Valverde, Juan. *Historia de la composicion del cuerpo humano.* Rome, A. Salamanca, 1556. [12], 105*ll.* + illustrations and legends.
[31] Trueta, Josep. *The spirit of Catalonia.* London, New York [etc.], G. Cumberlege, Oxford University Press, 1946. viii, 198 pp. [pp. 138–151]
[32] Colombo, R. *De re anatomica libri XV.* Venice, ex typographia N. Beuilacquae, 1559. 4 *ll.*, 169 [i.e. 269] pp.
[33] See Bainton, 1931 (note 27).

lesser circulation which is even clearer than that of Valverde; but both, as Trueta points out, would appear to be based on the description of Servetus. The passage in Colombo reads:

Between the ventricles is the septum, through which almost all think there is a way from the right ventricle to the left, so that the blood in transit may be rendered subtle by the generation of the vital spirits in order that the passage may take place more easily. This, however, is an error; for the blood is carried by the arterial vein [pulmonary artery] to the lung. . . . It is brought back thence together with air by the vein-like artery [pulmonary vein] to the left ventricle of the heart. This fact no one has hitherto observed or recorded in writing; yet it may be most readily seen by anyone.

As mentioned earlier, Colombo's manuscript had been many years in preparation, and his statement that no one had hitherto recorded the lesser circulation in writing was no doubt penned prior to the appearance of Valverde's book in 1556.

The description of the lesser circulation has therefore been a source of controversy and conjecture for the past two hundred and fifty years. If the contemporaries of Servetus were familiar with his disclosure, they chose not to mention it lest they too should meet his fate. Harvey seventy-five years later still had no knowledge of it; indeed the first public reference to Servetus' account occurs in a volume by the English antiquary, William Wotton, entitled *Reflections on Ancient and Modern Learning*, published in England in 1694.[34] Thus Wotton wrote (p. 211):

The first step that was made towards it [discovery of the circulation of the blood], was, the finding that the whole Mass of the Blood passes through the Lungs, by the Pulmonary Artery and Vein. The first that I could ever find, who had a distinct *Idea* of this Matter, was *Michael Servetus*, a *Spanish* Physician, who was burnt for *Arianism*, at *Geneva*, near 140 Years ago. . . . In a Book of his, intituled, *Christianismi Restitutio*, printed in the Year MDLIII. he clearly asserts, that the Blood passes

---

[34] Wotton, W. *Reflections on ancient and modern learning.* London, J. Leake for Peter Buck, 1694. 15 *ll.*, 359, 49 pp. In the second edition of Wotton's book, issued in 1697, he gives further details. In a postscript to his preface he states, among other things, that he had by this time actually seen a MS. of the 'Restitutio.' This postscript occurs also on pages 44–55 of a 55-page addendum intended to bring the first edition up to date and in some copies it is bound with the first edition. But Wotton in translating the quoted passage above obviously nodded and confused the right with the left side of the heart, which is not the case in the original Servetus text.

through the Lungs, from the Left to the Right Ventricle of the Heart; and not through the Partition which divides the two Ventricles, as was at that Time commonly believed. How he introduces it, or in which of the Six Discourses, into which *Servetus* divides his Book, it is to be found, I know not, having never seen the Book my self. Mr. *Charles Bernard,* a very learned and eminent Chirurgeon of *London,* who did me the Favour to communicate this Passage to me, (set down at length in the Margin) which was transcribed out of *Servetus,* could inform me no further, only that he had it from a learned Friend of his, who had himself copied it from *Servetus.*

In 1706 Leibnitz mentioned the Servetus discovery in a letter to La Croze, and the English medical bibliographer, James Douglas, wrote of it in 1715. In 1723, 252 pages of the *Christianismi restitutio* were reprinted in London by another antiquary;[35] but once again the whole edition was seized, on this occasion by order of the Bishop of London.[36] However, from this time on, Servetus' discovery began to be more freely acknowledged. A successful attempt at reprinting the book was made by the German Unitarian scholar, C. G. von Murr, in the year 1790 at Nuremberg. Ecclesiastical authorities frowned upon this undertaking also, but a fairly large edition finally found its way into print. It is a page-for-page reprint of the original text and is based on the copy in the Royal Library in Vienna which had been laboriously copied by a scribe, the text being set from the manuscript with surprisingly few misprints. This manuscript copy is now in the possession of the Houghton Library at Harvard University.[37] Whatever the size of this Murr reprinting may have been, it is now almost as rare as the Vienne original, of

---

[35] The antiquary in question was probably a Dutchman, Gysbert Dummer (L. L. Mackall; see Bibliotheca Osleriana, 1929, No. 839, p. 84). See also note 17.

[36] Copies of these pages are preserved in the Bibliothèque Nationale, London Medical Society, the British Museum (2 copies), Glasgow, and in Oxford at Christ Church and the Bodleian Library (proof sheets).

[37] Mr. W. A. Jackson has sent the following information: "On the fly-leaf is written—presumably in Murr's hand—'Summa Venerando Reinhardo d.d.g. de Murr d. 9 Apr. 1808.' On the verso of that leaf is the inscription 'a. 1786 Biblioth. Caesareae illato*), e Vindobonensi exemplo, typis excuso MS. olim Preussiani meminit, apud Ioh. Laur. Moshemium in hist. lat. Michaelis Serveti, pag. 204, et in germanice 1748 pag. 344. C. T. de Murr.' This is evidently the very transcript used by Murr for his reprint. . . . We have no further record of how the manuscript came to us, or just when."

*) In fronte huius exempli ad dextram subscriptum legitur: *Danielis Márkos Szent-Iványi Transylvano-Hungari. Londini 1665. die 13 Maii.* Hocce exemplum idem est, de quo Samuel Crellius in limine codicis MS. olim Preussiani meminit, apud Ioh. Laur. Moshemium in hist. lat. Michaelis Serveti, pag. 204, et in germanice 1748 pag. 344. C. T. de Murr.' This is evidently the very transcript used by Murr for his reprint. . . . We have no further record of how the manuscript came to us, or just when."

which three copies are known to have survived (Vienna, Paris, and Edinburgh).[38]

In 1924 another source from which Servetus might have learned of the circulation was discovered, namely a thirteenth century manuscript by Ibn an-Nafis of Persia.[39] Here one finds a well described account of the pulmonary circulation and denial of the existence of pores in the cardiac septum. Arabic and Persian writers infiltrated Spain during the Middle Ages; and while no copy of this manuscript has come to light in the places where Servetus is known to have worked, it is a well established fact that Servetus could read some Arabic. Temkin,[40] however, points out that Servetus was silent about the septal pores and that he differs from Ibn an-Nafis on other points in anatomy; from this Temkin thinks it improbable that Servetus had any knowledge of his Arabic predecessors. Temkin writes:

The contrasting views of Ibn an-Nafis and Servetus may be stated as follows: 1. Ibn an-Nafis denies the existence of pores in the septum of the heart. Servetus is silent on this point and does not exclude the possibility of blood sweating through. 2. Ibn an-Nafis thinks that the blood filters through the wall of the pulmonary artery, mixes with the air in the lungs, and then filters into the pulmonary vein. Servetus believes that the blood passes from the pulmonary artery into the pulmonary vein by way of intermediate vessels. If these interpretations are correct it would mean that in two rather important anatomical details Servetus differed from Ibn an-Nafis. This difference in its turn would give support to the belief that he had no knowledge of his Arabic predecessor.

Not only has recognition come slowly to Servetus, but there are some who doubt that he deserves credit for this highly important disclosure because he was far removed from medicine and was not himself an experimentalist. The eminent Mexican medical historian,

---

[38] There was originally a fourth copy at Vienne but this was destroyed by fire in 1854 (see E. J. Savigné, *Le savant Michel Servet, victime de tous les fanatismes.* Vienne, 1907); the one which supposedly had survived in the Vatican Library turns out to be the Murr 1790 reprint which had been erroneously catalogued.

[39] The manuscript was unknown to the Western world until 1924 when it was discovered by a modern Arabic scholar, Muhyi ad-Din at-Tatāwi, but it was not fully described until 1935—see Max Meyerhof, "Ibn an-Nafis (XIIIth cent.) and his theory of the lesser circulation." *Isis,* 1935, *23,* 100–120.

[40] Temkin, Owsei. "Was Servetus influenced by Ibn an-Nafis?" *Bull. Hist. Med.,* 1940, *8,* 731–734.

Izquierdo[41] is among those who hold this view. On the other hand, we have Guinterius' contemporary appraisal of Servetus, *i.e.,* the reference to his distinguished work in the dissecting room,[42] and we have already mentioned his highly successful therapeutic treatise on syrups. He moreover practised medicine at Vienne for some twelve years. Trueta points out also that not only did he give the excellent description of the lesser circulation but that he was familiar with the valves of the heart and how they functioned.

Chapter IV

CONCLUSIONS

ICHAEL SERVETUS, theological reformer, scholar, geographer, astrologist, lawyer, mathematician, physician, and spiritual founder of the modern Unitarian movement, was responsible in 1546, or possibly earlier, for stating in a manuscript and later publicly in print (*Christianismi restitutio,* published in 1553) that the blood passes from the right to the left side of the heart by going through the lungs and that during this passage is "refreshed" by absorbing something from the air. Servetus did not speculate upon the greater circulation, but it is possible that he had envisioned it. It is interesting that his aim in describing the circulation of the blood through the lungs was not to announce a new physiological discovery but rather the course taken by the spirit (*spiritus*) and the *anima.* The passage of blood through the lungs was cited only for this purpose.

The earlier Arabic writer, Ibn an-Nafis, a thirteenth century physician, has left a manuscript which indicates that he, too, had grasped the significance of the lesser circulation; the manuscript was probably unknown to Servetus and to the rest of the Western world until 1924 when it was discovered by a modern Arabic scholar, Muhyī ad-Dīn at-Tatawī.

---

[41] See note 27.
[42] Cushing, Harvey. *A bio-bibliography of Andreas Vesalius.* New York, Schuman's, 1943, pp. 49–50. See also Streeter, note 5.

Servetus' published version describing his discovery of the lesser circulation of the blood through the lungs had thus appeared in 1553, but there were two other accounts, one by Juan Valverde de Hamusco, published in Spanish at Rome in 1556, and another by Realdo Colombo, issued at Venice in 1559. The Valverde and Colombo versions follow that of Servetus closely and there is some reason to believe that both were based, unacknowledged, on the Servetus description—unacknowledged because Servetus had been burned at the stake for heresy and thereafter no one dared quote from any of his published works for fear of attack by the Inquisition.

Although we do not know how Servetus happened to arrive at his knowledge of the pulmonary circulation, it is clear that he knew the essential facts and that he accordingly deserves credit for one of the great discoveries in the history of medicine. He moreover stands as one of the preëminent figures of his century, for his brilliant and penetrating mind led him to make contributions in many other spheres. He was an important forerunner of modern biblical criticism and the founder of the science of comparative geography. Acknowledged a heretic in his time, now, four hundred years later, by virtue of his convictions and fearless defence of his unitarian faith, his lonely life and martyr's death, he has taken his rightful place among those gallant spirits who paid the supreme price for what they held as Truth.

Part II.

BIBLIOGRAPHY AND SOURCE MATERIALS

CHRISTIANI-
SMI RESTITV,
TIO.

*Totius ecclesiæ apostolicæ est ad sua limina vo-
catio, in integrum restituta cognitione Dei, fidei
Christi, iustificationis nostræ, regenerationis bapti
smi, & cœnæ domini manducationis. Restituto de
nique nobis regno cælesti, Babylonis impiæ captiuitate soluta, & Antichristo cum suis penitus destructo.*

בעת ההיא יעמוד מיכאל השר

και ἐγένετο πόλεμος ἐν τῷ οὐρανῷ.

M· D· LIII·

Fig. 6. Title-page of the copy of the *Christianismi restitutio* in the Bibliothèque
Nationale, Paris, and reproduced with their kind permission. [See pages 36, 84].

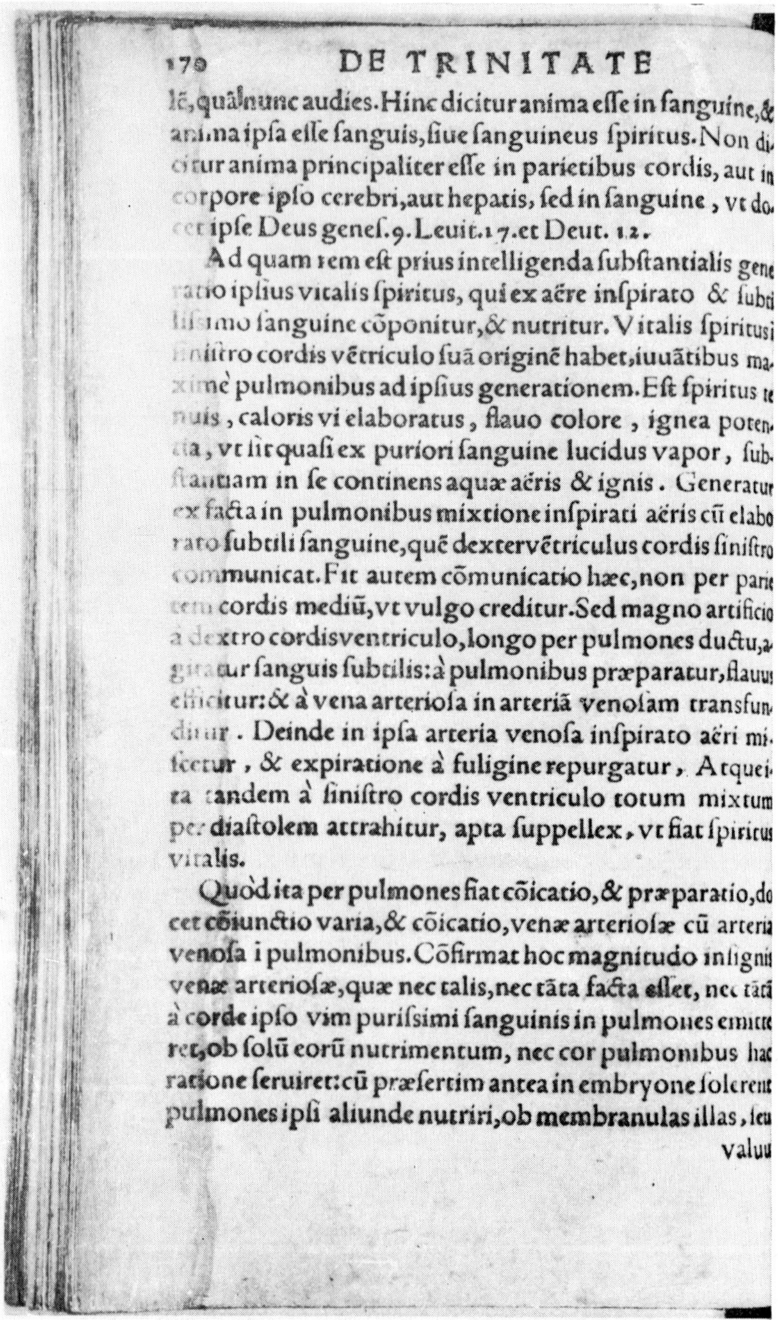

lé, quâ nunc audies. Hinc dicitur anima esse in sanguine, &
anima ipsa esse sanguis, siue sanguineus spiritus. Non dicitur anima principaliter esse in parietibus cordis, aut in
corpore ipso cerebri, aut hepatis, sed in sanguine, vt docet ipse Deus genes. 9. Leuit. 17. et Deut. 12.

Ad quam rem est prius intelligenda substantialis gene-
ratio ipsius vitalis spiritus, qui ex aëre inspirato & subti-
lissimo sanguine cõponitur, & nutritur. Vitalis spiritus
in sinistro cordis vẽtriculo suã originẽ habet, iuuãtibus ma-
xime pulmonibus ad ipsius generationem. Est spiritus te-
nuis, caloris vi elaboratus, flauo colore, ignea poten-
tia, vt sit quasi ex puriori sanguine lucidus vapor, sub-
stantiam in se continens aquæ aëris & ignis. Generatur
ex facta in pulmonibus mixtione inspirati aëris cũ elabo-
rato subtili sanguine, quẽ dexter vẽtriculus cordis sinistro
communicat. Fit autem cõmunicatio hæc, non per parie-
tem cordis mediũ, vt vulgo creditur. Sed magno artificio
à dextro cordis ventriculo, longo per pulmones ductu, a-
gitatur sanguis subtilis: à pulmonibus præparatur, flauus
efficitur: & à vena arteriosa in arteriã venosam transfunditur. Deinde in ipsa arteria venosa inspirato aëri mi-
scetur, & expiratione à fuligine repurgatur, Atquei-
ta tandem à sinistro cordis ventriculo totum mixtum
per diastolem attrahitur, apta suppellex, vt fiat spiritus
vitalis.

Quòd ita per pulmones fiat cõicatio, & præparatio, docet cõiunctio varia, & cõicatio, venæ arteriosæ cũ arteria
venosa i pulmonibus. Cõfirmat hoc magnitudo insigni
venæ arteriosæ, quæ nec talis, nec tãta facta esset, nec tãtã
à corde ipso vim purissimi sanguinis in pulmones emitte-
ret, ob solũ eorũ nutrimentum, nec cor pulmonibus hac
ratione seruiret: cũ præsertim antea in embryone solerent
pulmones ipsi aliunde nutriri, ob membranulas illas, seu
                                                    valuu

Fig. 7. Page 170 of the *Christianismi restitutio* containing the essential part of Servetus'
description of the lesser circulation. [See page 38].

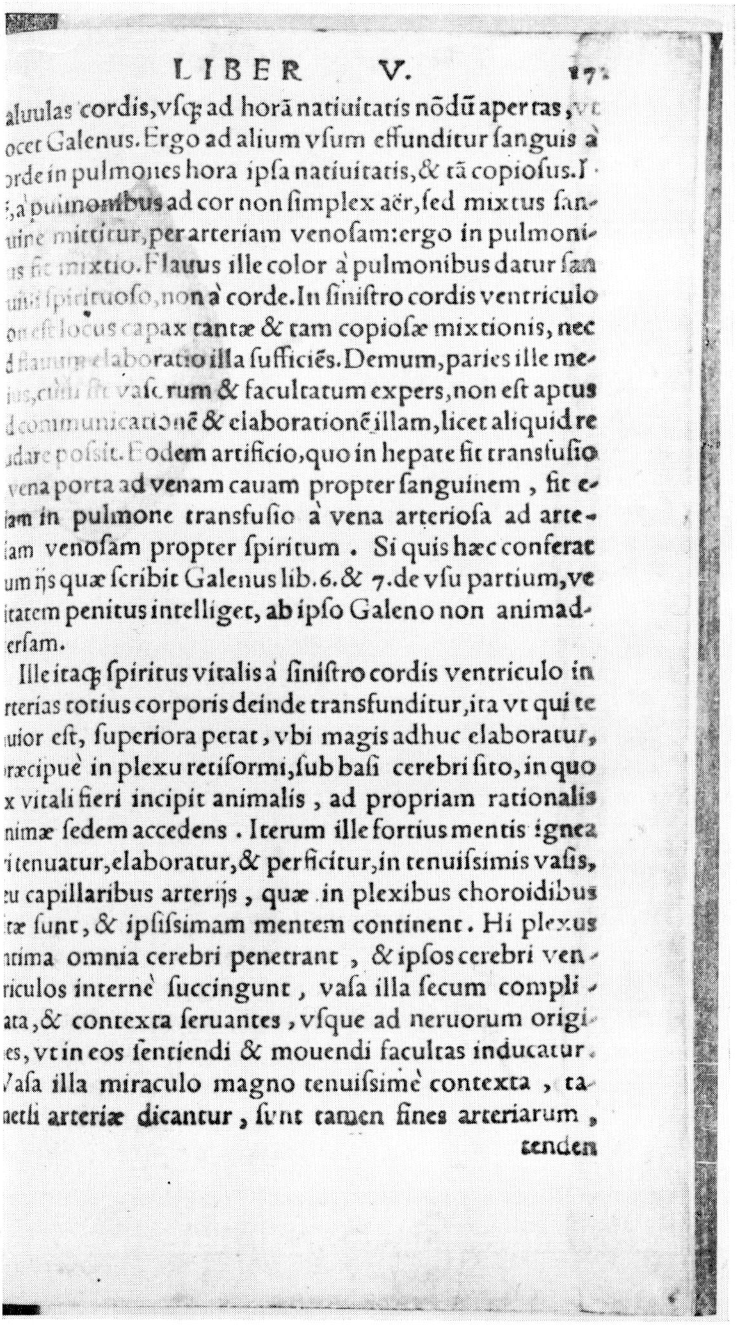

aluulas cordis, vſcɞ ad horā natiuitatis nōdū apertas, vt
ocet Galenus. Ergo ad alium vſum effunditur ſanguis à
ɔrde in pulmones hora ipſa natiuitatis, & tā copioſus. I ·
ɜ,à pulmonibus ad cor non ſimplex aër, ſed mixtus ſan-
uine mittitur, per arteriam venoſam: ergo in pulmoni-
ɪs ſit mixtio. Flauus ille color à pulmonibus datur ſan-
uni ſpirituoſo, non à corde. In ſiniſtro cordis ventriculo
on eſt locus capax tantæ & tam copioſæ mixtionis, nec
d ſlauum elaboratio illa ſufficiēs. Demum, paries ille me-
ius, cūi ſit vaſc rum & facultatum expers, non eſt aptus
d communicatiōē & elaboratiōē illam, licet aliquid re
dare poſsit. Eodem artificio, quo in hepate ſit transfuſio
vena porta ad venam cauam propter ſanguinem, ſit e-
am in pulmone transfuſio à vena arterioſa ad arte-
lam venoſam propter ſpiritum . Si quis hæc conferat
um ijs quæ ſcribit Galenus lib. 6. & 7. de vſu partium, ve
itatem penitus intelliget, ab ipſo Galeno non animad-
erſam.

Ille itacɞ ſpiritus vitalis à ſiniſtro cordis ventriculo in
rterias totius corporis deinde transfunditur, ita vt qui te
uior eſt, ſuperiora petat, vbi magis adhuc elaboratur,
ræcipuè in plexu retiformi, ſub baſi cerebri ſito, in quo
x vitali fieri incipit animalis , ad propriam rationalis
nimæ ſedem accedens . Iterum ille fortius mentis ignea
i tenuatur, elaboratur, & perficitur, in tenuiſsimis vaſis,
u capillaribus arterijs , quæ in plexibus choroidibus
ɪtæ ſunt, & ipſiſsimam mentem continent. Hi plexus
ntima omnia cerebri penetrant , & ipſos cerebri ven-
riculos internè ſuccingunt , vaſa illa ſecum compli-
ata, & contexta ſeruantes , vſque ad neruorum origi-
es, vt in eos ſentiendi & mouendi facultas inducatur.
Vaſa illa miraculo magno tenuiſsimè contexta , ta-
netli arteriæ dicantur , ſunt tamen fines arteriarum ,
                                                    tenden

Fig. 8. Page 171 of the *Christianismi restitutio* containing the essential part of Servetus'
description of the lesser circulation. (Courtesy of the Bibliothèque Nationale, Paris).

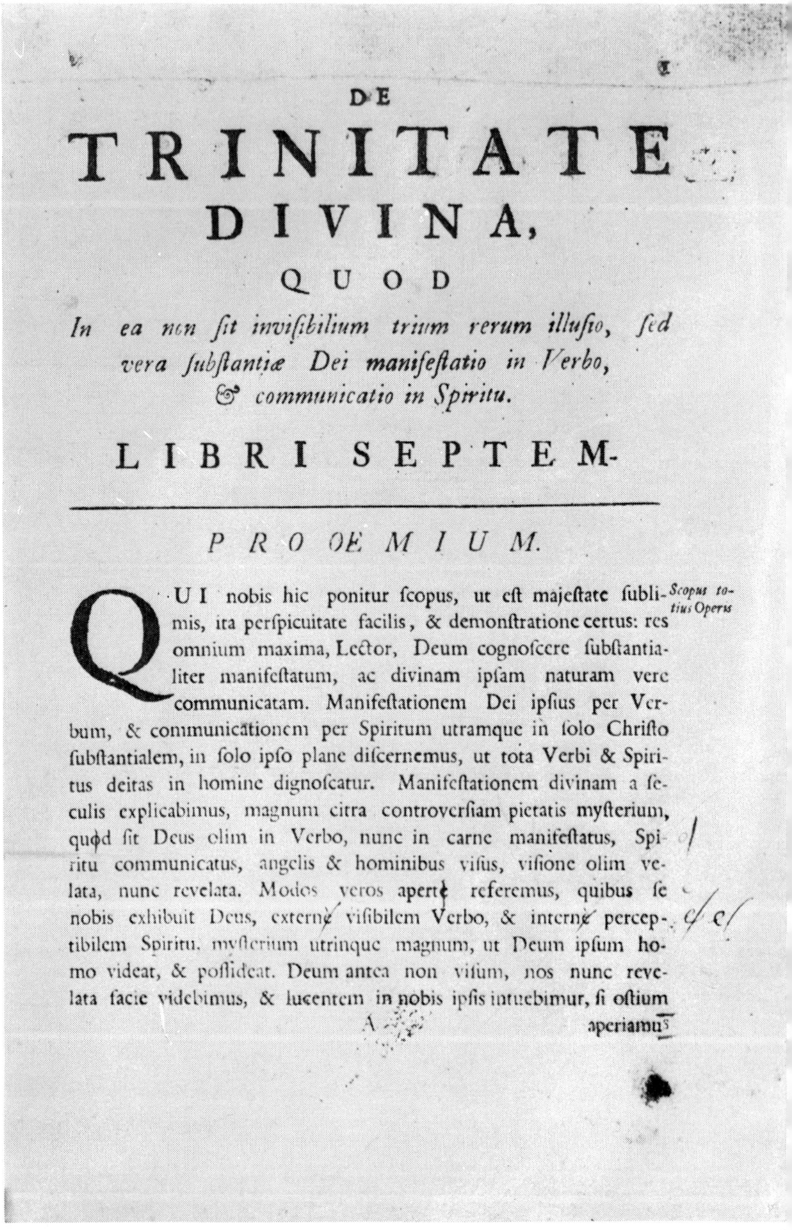

DE

TRINITATE
DIVINA,
QUOD

*In ea non fit invifibilium trium rerum illufio, fed
vera fubftantiæ Dei manifeftatio in Verbo,
& communicatio in Spiritu.*

LIBRI SEPTEM-

PROOEMIUM.

*Scopus to-
tius Operis*

Q UI nobis hic ponitur fcopus, ut eft majeftate fubli-
mis, ita perfpicuitate facilis, & demonftratione certus: res
omnium maxima, Lector, Deum cognofcere fubftantia-
liter manifeftatum, ac divinam ipfam naturam vere
communicatam. Manifeftationem Dei ipfius per Ver-
bum, & communicationem per Spiritum utramque in folo Chrifto
fubftantialem, in folo ipfo plane difcernemus, ut tota Verbi & Spiritus deitas in homine dignofcatur. Manifeftationem divinam a fe-
culis explicabimus, magnum citra controverfiam pietatis myfterium,
quod fit Deus olim in Verbo, nunc in carne manifeftatus, Spiritu communicatus, angelis & hominibus vifus, vifione olim ve-
lata, nunc revelata. Modos veros aperte referemus, quibus fe
nobis exhibuit Deus, externe vifibilem Verbo, & interne percep-
tibilem Spiritu, myfterium utrinque magnum, ut Deum ipfum ho-
mo videat, & poffideat. Deum antea non vifum, nos nunc revelata facie videbimus, & lucentem in nobis ipfis intuebimur, fi oftium

A

aperiamus

Fig. 9. Proof-sheet of the first page of the fragment of the *Christianismi restitutio*
printed at London in 1723. (Kindness of the Bodleian Library, Oxford). [See page 88].

Chapter V

BIBLIOGRAPHY OF SERVETUS

Explanatory Note

The bibliography of Servetus, though not long, is fraught with many pitfalls. This is due in part to the thorough fashion in which Calvin and others succeeded in having his books confiscated. The controversial nature of the texts and the partisanship that they have evoked over the past four centuries have not served to clarify the situation, nor the fact that Servetus' contribution to several of the works from the Lyons presses was not always recognized in print. Baudrier painstakingly pursued old records at Lyons and established Servetus' relationships with certain publishers' undertakings in that city, particularly with the Bible; there are many others, however, in which he is supposed to have played a major editorial rôle which have not yet been so verified. Thus d'Artigny (1749), after mentioning the 1542 Bible, goes on to say: "Il corrigea ensuite plusieurs livres pour Jean Frellon entr'autres une Somme Espagnol de S. Thomas, dont il fit les argumens. Il traduisit encore de Latin en Espagnol divers traités de grammaire; ainsi qu'il est marqué dans la déposition de Jean Frellon, du 23 Mai, 1553."

Where it is reasonable to suppose that an edition may have existed, it has been included, with a brief statement on the supporting evidence. In a few instances the description has had to be taken from secondary sources; in these circumstances the authority used has been cited. As this book goes to press the volume commemorating Servetus and Castellion, which was prepared under the direction of Professor B. Becker of Amsterdam, has just appeared. Professor Kot's paper therein has given much helpful data, particularly in connection with the various fragments of the *Christianismi restitutio* which were published. Professor Kot is continuing his work on the subject and hopes soon to add at least one more item to the bibliography of Servetus, alas too late for this present volume.

About two hundred and fifty libraries received copies of a short-title list of Servetus' writings with the request that they indicate their holdings. Most of these libraries, both in Europe and America, were connected either with universities or public institutions. It is recognized that many more small municipal and theological libraries might have been approached, but all the more obvious ones were questioned. There are certain discrepancies between former listings of library holdings such as those of Baudrier and Wilbur, but some of these may be attributed to the passage of time and the exigencies of war (many items having been destroyed in the bombings) and others to indifferent checking. So far as possible this latter situation has been corrected by subsequent correspondence, and it is hoped that the lists showing the location of the various items are reasonably correct.

The general literature bearing upon Servetus is vast, and no attempt has been made even to bring all the biographical and physiological papers together. Much of the information they contain is contradictory, and many of the papers perpetuate old errors and conflicts and must be read with caution. The careful and judicious studies of Prof. Bainton and Dr. Wilbur have been of great assistance, and Servetus scholars await with eager interest Prof. Bainton's biography of Servetus upon which he has been working for many years and which is to appear this year. Alexander Gordon's brief account of Servetus in the eleventh edition of the *Encyclopædia Britannica* is one of the most quoted, and Osler's attractive essay paints a colourful picture. As mentioned earlier, in view of Wilbur's recent bibliography no attempt is here made to cover the literature pertaining to Servetus' religious views.

Helpful bibliographical details are given in the *Bibliotheca Osleriana,* by van der Linde, Mackall, Wilbur, and others. In a few instances references that have already appeared in footnotes are repeated for greater accessibility in the list of source materials in the final chapter.

Here, too, will be found full citations of articles mentioned in the text only by author's name and date.

DE TRINI⸗
TATIS ERRORIBVS
LIBRI SEPTEM.

Per Michaelem Serueto, aliâs
Reues ab Aragonia
Hiſpanum.

Anno M· D. XXXI.

Fig. 10. Title of *De trinitatis erroribus,* 1531.

I. ON THE ERRORS OF THE TRINITY

1.

DE TRINITATIS ERRORIBUS Original ed. [*Hagenau*] 1531

Title (Fig. 10): De Trinitatis erroribus libri septem. Per Michaelem Serveto, aliâs Reves ab Aragonia Hispanum. Anno M. D. XXXI.

Collation: 8vo. Italic type (except for initial words of chapters and name of Deity which are printed in roman capitals); a-p⁸; 119 + [1] *ll.*

Contents: a1*a* title, a1*b* blank; a2*a*-p7*b* text; p8*a* erratum, p8*b* blank.

Note: Servetus was unable to find any printer in Basel or Strasburg willing to publish his book, and it was finally done at Hagenau, just north of Strasburg, by the press of Johann Setzer (Secerius). Even he could not have felt completely happy in the undertaking as he put neither his name nor the town on the title-page, though his work must easily have been recognized (the initial letter I on a2 being one of the distinguishing marks).
    The size of the edition is not known but was probably not large, and in the ensuing uproar many copies were doubtless destroyed. Wilbur (1932) states that at the trial in 1553 no copy "could be discovered to introduce in evidence. The rarity of the originals led to the making of manuscript copies, which are to be found in libraries almost as frequently as the originals." However, judging from the results of the present census, the volume is actually not so rare as has often been stated.

Copies: Aberdeen, Aix, Bern, Copenhagen, Edinburgh,¹ Florence, Geneva, Göttingen, Grenoble, The Hague, London,¹,² Madrid, Manchester,² Munich,¹,² Oxford,¹,³ Paris, ⁴,⁷,⁸ Stockholm,¹ Strasbourg, Stuttgart,¹ Utrecht, Vienna,¹ Zürich. CaMM-Os, CtY-M, DLC, MBM, MH, MdBJ-W, NIC, NNNAM, NNUT.
    There are two copies in the British Museum, and two also in the Bodleian Library, one

of which is bound with No. 5 (*q.v.*). At the R. Biblioteca Nazionale Centrale in Rome there is a manuscript copy in a seventeenth century hand. The volume at Geneva was Farel's copy (see Fig. 1). That in the Osler Library (No. 7765) was a gift from L. L. Mackall and carries the bookplate of Henry B. H. Beaufoy, F.R.S.; it was used by Earl Morse Wilbur in making his English translation (see No. 4). The Houghton Library at Harvard University has two MS. copies, one of the 16th, the other of the 17th century. Their printed copy is in a Count Hoym binding.

Copy used: Yale, purchased by Dr. Harvey Cushing in January 1934 from Blackwell's catalogue 341, lot 1580. It came from the library of the Bouverie Pusey family, Edward Bouverie Pusey (1800–1882) having been Regius Professor of Hebrew at Oxford and Canon of Christ Church.

DE TRINI-
TATIS ERRORIBVS
LIBRI SEPTEM.

*Per Michaelem Serueto, aliàs
Reues ab Aragonia
Hiſpanum.*

Anno M. D. XXXL

Fig. 11. Title of the spurious edition of
De trinitatis erroribus, published in 1721.

2.

DE TRINITATIS ERRORIBUS Spurious ed. [*Regensburg,* 1721?]

Title (Fig. 11): [Identical with preceding, except for the single hyphen that has replaced the double one and the grave accent in aliàs replacing the circumflex.]

Collation: Identical with preceding.

Note: The original edition having become very scarce, Georg Serpilius, called by Wilbur an "enterprising Lutheran superintendent" and by Mackall a "prominent clergyman and learned hymnologist," had a new printing made at Regensburg in 1721. The fact that Serpilius is known to have owned a copy of the 1665 *Religio medici* leads Mackall to momentary leniency, but he gives strong proof of the fact that this edition of the *Errors* was produced with intent to deceive so that it could command the high price of the original edition. It is thought that the *Errors* and the *Dialogues* were originally published separately, but in most instances they are to-day found bound together.

The use of the single hyphen on the title-page is the most obvious way to distinguish the counterfeit edition from the original. This difference continues throughout the text, the original edition having the double, the counterfeit the single hyphen. Dr. Wilbur has counted over 2150 instances of typographical differences in the two editions, more than two-thirds of which are "mere matters of punctuation, abbreviations, capitals, accents, spacing, and the like, . . . 25 typographical errors in the original are corrected, nearly an equal number are allowed to stand, and half as many new errors are incurred." Knowing the rarity of the original, Serpelius did not have to concern himself overmuch with perfection in his counterfeit. [Mr. Reichner points out that another way of identifying the counterfeit edition is the slanting italic capital letters which are found only in the eighteenth century, not earlier.]

Copies: Aberdeen, Brussels, Cambridge,[1] Copenhagen,[1] Dublin, Durham, Edinburgh,[2] Göttingen, The Hague, Leiden, London, [2,4] Madrid, Milan, Munich, [1,2] Pavia, Rome,[2] Strasbourg, Turin, Vienna.[1] CaMM-Os, CtY-M, MBM, NN, NNC, NNNAM, PPCP, RPB

Copy used: Yale, bound with the 'Dialogues' in original vellum; from the library of Professor Thilo, purchased in 1854.

3.

DE TRINITATIS ERRORIBUS Dutch trans. [Amsterdam] 1620

Title (Fig. 12): Van de Dolinghen in de Drievvldigheyd, Seven Boecken, Eertijds in Latijn beschreven Door Michiel Servetus, gheseyt Reves van Aragonien, Spaenjaerd: Ende Nu ghetreuvvelijck overgeset in onse Nederlandsche tale Door R. T. Hier sijn noch byghevoegt eenige andere kleyne tractaetjens van den selven Auteur. [Three Biblical quotations in Dutch.] Ghedruckt In't jaer ons Heeren 1620.

Collation: 4to. A-Z⁴, Aa-Cc⁴; 104 *ll.*, wrongly numbered 110.

Contents: A1*a* title, A1*b* blank; A2*a*-4*a* R.T.'s Voor-reden, A4*b* list of tractates (Fig. 13) B1*a*-Cc3*b* text, Cc4 blank.

Note: This is the only translation known to have been made before the English rendering by Wilbur in 1932 (No. 4). The translator, Reinier Telle or Regnerus Vitellius (1578–1618),[43] evidently wished, to judge from his preface, to offset some of the harsh things that had been said of Servetus. Though a Calvinist, he leaned toward Arminianism and he was warned by Episcopius, the Remonstrant professor at Leiden, that the book would almost certainly arouse further dissension at an already troubled period. Publication was therefore delayed for six years, by which time Telle was dead. This circumstance may account in part for the many physical errors that the book contains. The foliation is particularly bad; folios 5–8 are lacking, 16 is wrongly numbered 15, 19 wrongly numbered 18, 57 wrongly numbered 61, and the leaves following 88 are numbered 89, 91, 93, 95, 96, 97, 98, 101, 100, 105, 102, 109, 104,—and then are correct to 110. There is no place of publication given in the book; but Telle having lived and taught in Amsterdam, it has generally been assumed that the book was printed there.

Copies: Amsterdam, Basel, Bonn, Brussels, Ghent, Göttingen, The Hague, Halle, Leiden, Leipzig, London,[1] Madrid, Manchester, [1,2] Naples, Oxford,[1,4] Paris, [4,6] Strasbourg, Stuttgart,[1] Upsala,[2] Vienna,[1] Zürich. CaMM-Os, DLC, ICU, MH, MdBJ-W, NIC, NNUT.

---

[43] A careful study of Telle and his part in the translation of *De trinitatis erroribus* by the Director of the Library of the University of Amsterdam, H. de la Fontaine Verwey, has just appeared. In it he gives Telle's dates as 1558 or 1559–1619 or 1620 as opposed to those here quoted from van der Linde.

Van te Dolinghen inde
DRIE VVLDIGHEYD,

Seven Boecken/

Eertijds in Latijn beschreven

Door

MICHIEL SERVETVS, gheseyt

Reves van Aragonien, Spaenjaerd:

Ende

Nu ghetrouvvelijck overgeset in onse
Nederlandsche tae,

Door

R. T.

Hier sijn noch byghevoegt eenige andere kleyne
tractaetjens van den selven Auteur.

1. THESS. 5.

Proeft alle dingen, ende behout het goede.

1. IOAN. 4.

En gelooft niet eenen yeg licken geeste, maer
beproeft de geesten of sy uy: God sijn.

MATTH. 15.

Alle plantinge, die mijn hemelsche Vader niet
gheplant en heeft, sal uytgeroeyt vvorden.

Ghedruckt
In't jaer ons Heeren 1620.

Fig. 12. Title-page of the Dutch translation of *De trinitatis er-*
roribus made by Renier Telle and published in 1620 after his
death. (Kindness of the Welch Medical Library).

Copies used: Welch Medical Library and Cornell University. Mr. L. L. Mackall gave two copies to his Alma Mater, Johns Hopkins University; one measures 18.8 by 14 cm. and is bound in full red morocco, the other is 19.5 by 14.5 cm. in size and is bound with *Historie van Michael Servetus* (Rotterdam, 1729). The Cornell copy is bound in old vellum and has three leaves in front and four in back filled with notes in Dutch in a contemporary hand.

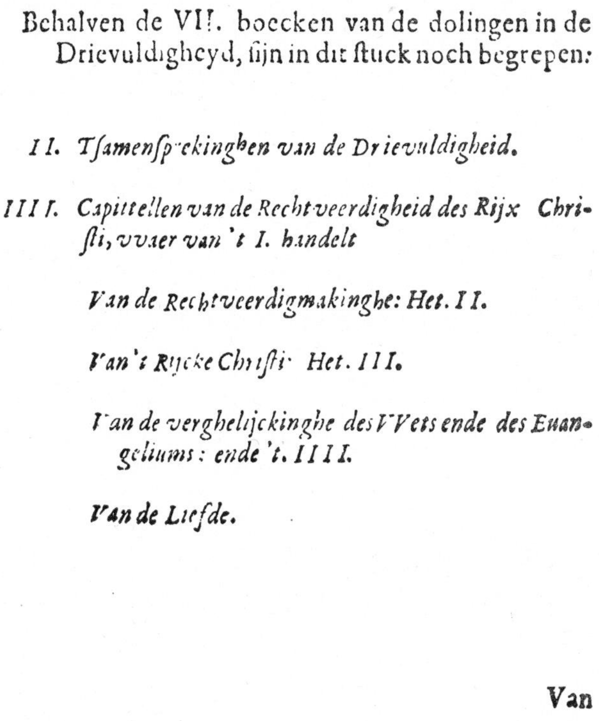

Behalven de VII. boecken van de dolingen in de
Drievuldigheyd, fijn in dit ftuck noch begrepen:

I I. *Tfamenfprekingben van de Drievuldigheid.*

III I. *Capittellen van de Rechtveerdigheid des Rijx Chrifti, vvaer van 't I. handelt*

Van de Rechtveerdigmakinghe: Het. I I.

Van 't Rijcke Chrifti Het. I I I.

*Van de verghelijckinghe des VVets ende des Euan-
gelinms: ende 't. I I I I.*

Van de Liefde.

Van

Fig. 13. Signature A4*b* of the Dutch translation of *De trinitatis erroribus* of 1620, with a list of tractates the volume is supposed to contain.

4.
DE TRINITATIS ERRORIBUS English trans.

Cambridge, Mass., 1932

Title: On the errors of the Trinity. Seven books. By Michael Serveto, *alias* Reves, a Spaniard of Aragon. MDXXXI. *In:* The two treatises of Servetus on the Trinity. . . . Now first translated into English by Earl

Morse Wilbur, D.D. Cambridge, Harvard University Press; London: Humphrey Milford, Oxford University Press, 1932.

Collation (entire volume): 8vo. xxxviii, 264 pp.

Contents: p.[i] series half-title, p.[ii] series title, p.[iii] title, p.[iv] copyright, p.[v] contents, p.[vi] blank, pp.[vii]-xviii Introduction, pp.[xix]-xxviii Life of Servetus, pp.[xxix]-xxxvi Bibliography, pp.[xxxvii]-xxxviii Translator's note; p.[1] title-page of *Errors,* p.[2] blank, pp.[3]-5 Editor's 'Argument' and 'Synopsis,' pp.6-184 text of *Errors;* p.[185] title-page of *Dialogues,* p.[186] blank, p.[187] 'Synopsis,' pp. 188-264 text.

Note: This English translation appeared in Volume XVI of the *Harvard Theological Studies.* It is preceded by a most excellent introduction, a short account of Servetus, and a brief listing of Servetus' works and selected bibliographical references. Professor Wilbur has given the 'Argument' and 'Synopsis' at the head of each book; he has included all the marginalia, has given the signatures of the original edition throughout for greater ease in comparison, and by the generous use of footnotes he has done much to clarify allusions and identify quotations. All those who have attempted to follow the tangled threads of Servetus' original Latin will realize what a debt is owed to Professor Wilbur's careful scholarship.

Copies: As this modern text is still available, a census of copies will not be given. It may be of some interest, however, to note that only 18 copies were listed in foreign libraries and 12 in North America—this from a census of some two hundred libraries.

DIALOGO-
RVM DE TRINITATE
LIBRI DVO.

DE IVSTICIA REGNI CHRI-
sti, Capitula Quatuor.

PER MICHAELEM SERVETO,
alias Reues, ab Aragonia
Hispanum.

Anno M. D. XXXII.

Fig. 14. Title of *Dialogorum de Trinitate libri duo, 1532.*

II. DIALOGUES ON THE TRINITY

5.

DIALOGI DE TRINITATE Original ed.   [*Hagenau*] 1532

Title (Fig. 14): Dialogorum de Trinitate libri duo. De Iusticia regni Christi, capitula quatuor. Per Michaelem Serveto, *alias* Reves, ab Aragonia Hispanum. Anno M. D. XXXII.

Collation: 8vo. A-F⁸; 48 *ll.* without pagination or foliation.

Contents: A1*a* title, A1*b* To the reader; A2*a*-C6*a* text of Books I-II; C6*b*-F8*a* text of De justicia regni Christi, Chaps. I-IV.

Note: This second work from the pen of the twenty-one-year-old Servetus was also done at the press of Setzer although he himself had meanwhile died. The book is much more moderate in tone, but it did little to quiet the storm produced by the *Errors*. Sale of both works was forbidden at Basel and Strasburg; but the Catholics seem to have been far less concerned about it than were those who embraced the many different forms of Protestantism.

Copies: Aberdeen, Aix, Bern, Copenhagen, Florence, Freiburg im Breisgau, Geneva, Göttingen, The Hague, London,[1,2] Madrid, Manchester,[2] Munich,[1,2] Oxford,[1,3] Paris,[8] Stockholm,[1,2] Strasbourg, Utrecht, Vienna.[1] CtY-M, MBM, MdBJ-W, NNUT. The Royal College of Obstetrics and Gynaecology in London lists a manuscript, probably of the eighteenth century, of 156 pp. The Houghton Library at Harvard University has a MS. copy, but its date is not given. Columbia University Library also has a MS. copy, probably of the 17th or 18th century.

Copy used: Yale; bound with No. 1, *q.v.*

DIALOGO-
RVM DE TRINITATE
LIBRI DVO.

DE IVSTICIA REGNI CHRI-
fti , Capitula Quatuor.

PER MICHAELEM SERVETO,
aliâs Reues , ab Aragonia
Hifpanum.
Anno M. D. XXXII.

Fig. 15. Title of the spurious edition of the *Dialogues*
published in 1721.

6.

DIALOGI DE TRINITATE Spurious ed.   [*Regensburg, 1721?*]

Title (Fig. 15): [Identical with preceding except for the use of single rather than double hyphens.]

Collation: The same as in No. 5.

Note: Mackall (see footnote 17) calls attention to various differences in copies of this eighteenth century forgery. They are not, however, extensive and very probably occurred while the book was going through the press. An error in spelling on the title-page was corrected, ornamental initials on A2*a* and C6*b* were changed, perhaps because the ones first used were not sharp enough, etc. As stated earlier, in most instances this treatise was bound with I.2, but not always. The present census did not ask for information as to whether items were bound separately, and such details were not often vouchsafed. The Hispanic Society of America has two copies of this edition, each bound separately without the text of the *Errors.* They have the type variations mentioned above.

Copies: Aberdeen, Brussels, Cambridge,[1] Dublin, Edinburgh,[2] Göttingen, The Hague, Leiden, London,[2,4] Madrid, Milan, Munich,[1,2] Pavia, Rome,[2] Strasbourg, Turin. CtY-M, MBM, NN, NNC, NNH, NNNAM, PPCP, RPB.

Copies used: Yale: (i) bound with No. 2, *q.v.;* (ii) without the *Errors* and without type variations, in contemporary binding.

7.
DIALOGI DE TRINITATE Dutch trans.   [*Amsterdam*] 1620

Title (see Fig. 12): Hier sijn noch by ghevoegt eenige andere kleyne tractaetjens van den selven Auteur. . . . Ghedruckt in't jaer ons Heeren 1620.

Note: This promissory note on the title-page of the Dutch translation of the *Errors* has not been fulfilled so far as can be learned. It is quite possible that Telle prepared the text but that with the delay in publication the person or persons who saw the book through the press after his death simply omitted this section and failed to amend his original title and to delete the list of additional tracts (see Fig. 9). We include the title here since it has not actually been proved a ghost.[44]

8.
DIALOGI DE TRINITATE Engl. trans. *Cambridge, Mass.,* 1932

Title: Dialogues on the Trinity, two books. On the righteousness of Christ's kingdom, four chapters. By Michael Serveto, *alias* Reves, a Spaniard of Aragon. MDXXXII.

Collation: 8vo. pp.[185]-264 in: *The two treatises of Servetus on the Trinity.* . . . Now first translated into English by Earl Morse Wilbur, D.D. Cambridge, Harvard University Press; London: Humphrey Milford, Oxford University Press, 1932. xxxviii, 264 pp.

Note: See No. 4.

---

[44] See Verwey's recent paper for a fuller discussion of the circumstances surrounding this translation.

III. PTOLEMY'S GEOGRAPHY

9.

PTOLEMÆI GEOGRAPHICÆ ENARRATIONIS LIBRI OCTO

Lyons, 1535

Title (Fig. 16): Claudii Ptolemæi Alexandrini Geographicæ enarrationis libri octo. Ex Bilibaldi Pirckeymheri tralatione, sed ad Graeca & prisca exemplaria à Michaële Villanovano iam primum recogniti. Adiecta insuper ab eodem scholia, quibus exoleta urbium nomina ad nostri seculi more exponuntur. . . . Lugduni, ex officina Melchioris et Gasparis Trechsel fratrum. M. D. XXXV.

Colophon (n4*a* [p.151]): Excudebant Lugduni Melchior et Gaspar Trechsel Fratres M. D. XXXV.

Collation: Fol. Rom. and ital. types; a-m⁶, n⁴, 1-45², (46-47)², 48-50², A-E⁶, F⁸; 149 + [3] pp., 136 unnumb. *ll.*

Contents: a1*a* title; A1*b* 'Michael Villanovanus Lectori'; a2 Pirckheimer's dedication to Sebastian, bishop of Brescia; a3*a*-n3*a* (pp. 5-149) text; n3*b* table; n4*a* colophon, n4*b* blank; 1-1*a*—50-2*a* tables and maps, 50-2*b* blank; A1*a*-F8*a* index, F8*b* blank.

Note: This was the first of Servetus' published writings to carry the name Villanovanus. He undertook the revision of Ptolemy's *Geography* for the brothers Trechsel, using the text of the 1525 edition of Bilibaldus Pirckheimer. But he went back to manuscript and early printed editions to correct many errors that had crept in over the years, and into the new edition went much of his quite extraordinary erudition. Unfortunately he kept the passage about the Holy Land which Pirckheimer had used (and Phrisius before him), and this was introduced against him at his trial eighteen years later. The volume, a handsomely printed folio in double column, has the running-heads of the first part printed in flowing banners with figures at either end. The second section, "Principium Europae hae sunt e cognitis totius orbis provinciis . . .," contains 48 double-page maps and one single-page map (one leaf carries the sig. 46-47), with handsome woodcuts throughout.

Eloy Bullón y Fernández in his *Miguel Servet y la geografía del renacimiento* (2nd ed., Madrid, 1929; 3rd ed., 1945) reprinted the original Latin text of 'Michael Villanovanus to the Reader' and also the passage on the discovery of America (leaf 2 verso of quire 28). The text of these two passages as well as those on Britain & Ireland, Spain, France, Germany, Italy, and the Western Ocean of the New World has been translated into English by Professor O'Malley (pp. 18-37).

Copies: Augsburg, Bordeaux,[1,2] Brussels, Budapest, Cambridge,[2] Cracow, Edinburgh,[1] Ghent, Glasgow, London,[1] Lyons, Madrid, Munich,[1] Oxford,[1] Paris,[4,7] Stockholm,[1] Strasbourg, Stuttgart,[1] Upsala,[1] Zurich. CaMM-Os, CSmH, CtY, DLC, ICN, ICU, MH, MdBJ-W, NIC, NN, NNC, NNH, NNNAM, NNP, NjP, RPJCB.

Copies used: Bibliothèque National (M. de Manne) and Yale (Thorne Collection of Cartography and Geography). The latter copy measures 42.2 by 28.5 cm.

CLAVDII PTOLE-
MÆI ALEXANDRINI
GEOGRAPHICÆ ENAR-
RATIONIS
LIBRI OCTO.

EX BILIBALDI PIRCKEYMHERI
tralatione, ſed ad Græca & priſca exemplaria à Michaële Villanouano iam primum recogniti.
Adiecta inſuper ab eodem Scholia,
quibus exoleta urbium no-
mina ad noſtri ſecu
li morē expo
nuntur.
*

QVINQVAGINTA ILLÆ QVOQVE CVM
ueterum tum recentium tabulæ adnectuntur, uarijq;
incolentium ritus & mores
explicantur.

LVGDVNI
EX OFFICINA MELCHIORIS ET
GASPARIS TRECHSEL FRATRVM.
M. D. XXXV.

Fig. 16. Title-page of the first edition of Ptolemy's *Geography* to be edited by Servetus, 1535. (Kindness of Yale University Library).

10.

PTOLEMÆI GEOGRAPHICÆ ENARRATIONIS LIBRI OCTO
Lyons, 1541

Title (Fig. 17): Claudii Ptolemæi Alexandrini geographicæ enarrationis, libri octo. . . . à Michaèle Villanovano secondò recogniti. . . . Prostant Lugduni apud Hugonem à Porta, M. D. XLI.

Colophon ([2nd] h6*a*): Excudebat Gaspar Trechsel Viennæ M. D. XLI.

Collation: Fol. Rom. and ital. types; a-m⁶, n⁴, 1-45², (46-47)², 48-50², a-h⁶; 149 + [3] pp., 98 + 48 unnumb. *ll.*

Contents: a1*a* title, a1*b* 'Michael Villanovanus lectori' and four lines of verse 'Ad eundem' at the end (Fig. 18); a2*a* dedication to Archbishop Pierre Palmier, a2*b*-n3*b* text; n4*a* colophon, n4*b* blank; 1-50 maps and explanations; a1*a*-h5*b* index, h6*a* colophon, h6*b* blank.

Note: This is a much less elaborately printed volume than the 1535 edition, the many large woodcuts and the banner running-heads having been omitted. The general style, however, remains the same, and the maps have been printed from the same blocks. The book is now dedicated by Servetus to his patron, Archbishop Palmier,[45] and perhaps because of this fact many of the more critical statements of the earlier edition which had meanwhile caused so much criticism are now considerably softened. There are also some slight additions to the text as, for example, in the account of Scotland.

Copies: Bordeaux, Brussels, Cambridge,² Dublin, Edinburgh,¹ Glasgow, Grenoble, Lisbon, London,¹ Madrid, Munich,¹ Oxford,¹ Paris,⁷ Rome, Stockholm,² Strasbourg. CtY-M, DLC, Humbert, MH, MdBJ-W, NIC, NNH, RPJCB.

Copy used: Yale, purchased by Dr. Cushing from Wilfrid M. Voynich; it measures 39.8 by 27.1 cm.

11.

PTOLEMÆI GEOGRAPHICÆ ENARRATIONIS LIBRI OCTO
Spanish trans.   *Madrid,* 1932

Title: Descripciones geograficas del estado moderno de las regiones, en la geografia de Claudio Ptolomeo Alejandrino por Miguel Vilanovano (Miguel Servet) precedidas de una biografía del autor y traducidas del Latín por el Dr. José Goyanes Capdepvila [*sic*]. . . . Madrid, Imprenta y Encuadernación de Julio Cosano, 1932.

Title preceding translation [p.85]: Ocho libros de la narración geografica de Claudio Ptolomeo Alejandrino. Según la versión de Bilibaldo Pirckeim-

---

⁴⁵ This dedication is translated by O'Malley (pp. 192–194).

CLAVDII

PTOLEMAEI
ALEXAN:
DRINI

Geographicæ Enarrationis,
Libri Octo.

EX BILIBALDI PIRCKE.
ymheri tralatione, sed ad Græca & prisca exemplaria à Michaële Villanouano
secundò recogniti, & locis innumeris denuò castigati. Adiecta insuper ab eodem Scho
lia, quibus & difficilis ille Primus Liber nunc primum explicatur, & exoleta Vrbium
nomina ad nostri seculi morem exponuntur. Quinquaginta illæ ;quoque cum ueterum tum
recentium Tabulæ adnectuntur, uarijſ; incolentium ritus & mores explicantur.

*

Accedit Index locupletiſſ.mus hactenus non uiſus.

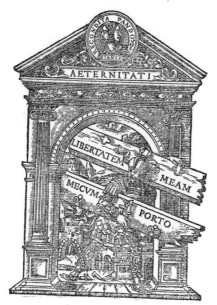

Prostant Lugduni apud Hugonem à Porta.

M. D. XLI.

Fig. 17. Title-page of Servetus' second editing of
Ptolemy's *Geography*, 1541.

MICHAEL VILLANOVANVS
LECTORI S.

ON ABRE *fuerit*,Lector amice,de Claudio noſtro paucula hic præſcribere,ac demum quid nos in hac editione præſtiterimus commeminiſci.Fuit Ptolemæus Alexandria Ægypti urbe regia oriundus,Græca literas,quibus tunc Ægyptus imbuebatur,abundè doctus:tametſi & Rhodi egerit aliquando:Philoſophus,Aſtrologus,iuxtà ac Mathematicus ſtrenuus,quod & alia eius monumenta teſtantur.Floruit ſub Traiano,Adriano,& Antonio Pio Cæſaribus.Tanta in orbe perluſtrando ſiue ſuit ſolertie plus quàm Herculea gloria,ut terrarum orbem ſine bello inuadens,ſub regulam quandam cenſeri coëgerit,& nobis fruëdum deſcriptum tradidevit.Nec id ſoli præſtitit,ſed cœleſtia terreſtribus coniunxit,eorú menſuras in unu collegit.Fuit Strabone,Plinio & Pomponio Mela poſterior,ſed qui illos & priores omnes in Geographico artificio facilè ſuperavit.Interpretes eius fuerunt Nicolaus Angelus Florëtinus,Ioannes Berëberus & Bilibaldus Pircheymherus.In priorë etiã librü annotatiões ſcripſit Berenherus,ſed ita,ut tã in eo quã in alijs multa deſyderëtur.Nos verò meliora quæq; ſequuti uires omnes ac neruos intendimus,in corruptis emendandis,& recluſis explicãdis,Periculoſus utraq; parte labor,nec alicui hactenus attentatius:ſed pius,& q ueniã nobis impetret,ſicubi locorũ lectori nõ fecerimus ſatis.Illud nè tacuerin ,ex alijs codicibus cũ græcis tũ latinis,alioruq; autorũ aſſidua lectiõe,locos ad multa milia nos reſtituiſſet:quorũ cëturias aliquot referre ope repreciumſoret,ut ſpecimen aliquod guſtauris præberetur,ſed unius Narbonenſis Galliæ exempla ſat erunt.Libro ij.capi.10.tabula 3.Europæ,Chetinæ ciuitas priùs legebatur,cum ex græco codice Betiræ fuerit legendum,quæ eſt Biterrenſis ciuitas,uulgo dicta Beſiers:Stephanus etiam Betarrã nominat:Mela,Plinius,& Strabo Blitt.ram. Foſſæ marine ibidem legebatur,cum Foſſas Marianas à Mario Ro.conſule dictas ſcriptores omnes teſtentur,quas nunc Aquas mortuas uocamus.Item flumen Sicarus ĩ altero exẽplari legebatur in altero Tiſara,cũ nuutro modo ſuerit legẽdũ,ſed Hiſera ſiue græcum exemplar,ſiue aliorum ſcripta,& maximè Cæſaris commentarios quis inſpiciat.aſtipulatur etiam hodiernum nomen quod idem fluuius uulgo retinet.Nec illos taceam qui pro Atari fluuio ibidë ſcripſerant Anar,& pro Dubi Buden,Cepero pro Ceſſero,Loauenniorum pro Auenniorum colonia ,Sempos populos pro Senņtijs,quos hodie Dignenſes.Omiſſa quoq; Cabelliorũ colonia duas Maſſilias fecere,alterã græcam,alteram non græcam.Orobius inſuper ſcribitur ibi fluuius,qui Obris ceteris dicitur.Emendaſſemus etiam ſi licuiſſet Tolofæ ſitum,qui ad Garumne,non ĩ lleris fluuij ripam conſiſtit. Sed ut nobis non licuit inueterata illas chorographicas tabula renouare,ita earum errata nobis adſcribi non debent.Longitudinum & latitudinum numeros,quos cmendauimus,ne cui ſim moroſus,hic ſubticebo,cum ij ſatis legenti & conferenti patuerint.Nec in ea re à Ptolemæi mente aſceſſimus,ſed tãtum iuxta priores typos librariorum reſtituimus errata.Libro octauo qui ſuprà alios,ſi Bilibaldo & Eraſmo credimus,caſtigatione deſyderabat,adnotatiunculam adiecimus,quæ etiam ſi totius ille liber perıret,ſacile quiuis uel mediocriter in Mathematicis peritus,non ſolum in urbibus à Ptolemæo ibi deſcriptis,ſed in alijs quibuſcunq;,maiorum dierum quantitates,& ab Alexandria diſtantias metiri queat.Illud item ſciendum,ſitue ordinem aliquando præpoſterum,nec eundem eſſe in Ptolemæi traditione & noſtra interpretatione,ſecundùm ab ipſo commiſſa trãſpoſitione locorũ.Vt inter Nemetos & Vangiones Germanos hodie populos in tabula Belgicæ Galliæ commemoratos:& inter Liburnũ portum & Populoniũ promontoriũ ſiue Populonia urbë in Tyrrheno Italiæ pelago.Nos enim uera nomina in margine reddidimus,ſed ipſe priores poſuit,qui eo quo ipſe ,pcedebat ordine poſteriores eſſe debuere.
Eodem littore inter Telamonem Hoſſam & Coſſas trãſpoſitio eſt.idem commiſſum in Alpium montium nominibus,quod Andreas Alciatus in Taciũ annotauit.In Liguriæ maritimis Iacobus Bracelleus ordinem à Ptolemæo alium nos docuit.Sed hactenus de ijs quæ corruptè legebãtur.Scholia deinceps adiecimus,quò lectio eſſet dilucidior ſuauior & planior:quæ quantum adiamenti lectori ſint allatura,eorũ eſto iudiciũ,qui lectionis uſu experimentũ fecerint.In euoluendis ſanè cum Græcorum tum Latinorum poëmatibus,hiſtorijs,& alijs ſcriptis:cã de regionibus,ciuitatibus,montibus,& fluminibus,quod per ſæpe fit,ſermo inciderit:ſi ſe tũc ad noſtri Ptolemæi lectionẽ quã deflectat:urbiũ uomina cum priſcis & poëtarum nominibus coniuncta,& ad noſtri temporis ſermonem coaptata,iucunditatis nonnihil pro culdubio lectori ſunt allatura:cum nuda Ptolemæi lectio parũ uenuſta hactenus uiſa ſit.Et quò magis tyronũ animos ad hanc lectionem intenderemus,materna lingua tanquam faciliore plurima urbiũ uocabula explicuimus:ut cum Gallis gallicè,cũ Germanis germanicè,cũ Italis Italicè,& cũ Hiſpanis hiſpanicè loqui uideremur:quorũ omniũ regiones uidimus,& linguas utcuq; nouimus.In reddendis ſermoni uernaculo urbiũ nominibus,ſcriptorũ autoritate ,ppria experiëtia,certiſſimus coniecturis,quoad eius fieri potuit ſumus connixi:in hac præſertim ſecundæ editione,in qua multa prioris errata caſtigauimus.Ceterum plurimas earum quæ à Ptolemæo ſunt deſcriptæ,cum ſint exciſæ,nos ſilentio præterimus.Aſt ubi deſolatarũ eodem aut proximo loco urbes alias ſucceſſere,nou.m ſtruct.m loco ſcriptæ deſtructæ ſubrogauimus,in margine quidem.nam ipſum Ptolemæi ſcriptum inuiolatum eſſe uoluimus.Qnam noſtra opera ram ad prouinciarum orbis notitiam & præſentium cum præteritis collationem,quæ ſuauis eſt exercitatio,maximè facere ,nemo,ni fallor,inficias ituur eſt:niſi zoilus quiſpiam ſit frontis ,pfricẏ,qui aliorũ ſudores nequeat ſine liuore dimetiri.Tu verò quiſquis ſis candidus lector,noſtras ſpero uigilias acceptas probataſ ; ſeres. Vale.

Ad eundem.

Si terras & regna hominum,ſi ingentia quæq;
Flumina,cœruleum ſi mare noſſe uuiat,
Si montes,ſi urbes populoq; opibusq; ſuperbas,
Huc ades,hæc oculis proſpice cuncta tuis.

Fig. 18. Michael Villanovanus to the Reader. From the 1541 edition of Ptolemy's *Geography*.

hery, y revisado por Miguel Vilanovano a tenor de los primitivos ejemplares griegos. Anádense además, por el mismo, unos scholios por los cuales se declaran los nombres de las ciudades según la costumbre de nuestro siglo. Editorial de Lyon de Melchor y Gaspar Treschel, Hermanos, 1535.

Collation: 8vo. 382 + [1] pp.

Contents: p.[1] series half-title, p.[3] series title; p.[5] title for the present work; pp. 7-83 account of Servetus' life; p.[85] translated title of the . Ptolemy; p.[87] half-title ("Estudio reciente de las regiones de Europa por Miguel Vilanovano"); pp.[89]-93 "Miguel Vilanovano saluda al Lector"; pp.[95]-207 translation of textual descriptions beginning on sig. 1-2*b* of original edition; p.[209] half title ("Exposición detallada de los dos procesos seguidos a Miguel Serveto tomados del libro del Dr. J. Goyanes *Miguel Serveto, teólogo, geógrafo y médico.* etc. Madrid, 1933"), pp.[211]-374 text, pp.[377]-382 index, p.[383] colophon.

Note: Page [3] is a title-page indicating that the book is Vol. X in the series, "Biblioteca clásica de la medicina española," issued by the Academia Nacional de Medicina. This carries the date 1932; but on p. [383] is the statement: "Este décimo tomo de la 'Biblioteca Clásica de la Medicina Española' acabóse de imprimir en Madrid, en la oficina de J. Cosano, Palma, 11, estando a la mira el Dr. Goyanes Capdevila, el 16 de septiembre de 1935. LAUS DEO." The linen cover of the volume, which has the full title of the book, has for the final line "Madrid.—Imp. de Cosano.—1935." As shown in the contents, the latter part of the volume is a reprinting of pages 224-327 from Professor Goyanes' earlier work.

Copies: No census was taken of this as the translation was not known when the original short-title list was circulated, and presumably the book is still in print.

IV. APOLOGY AGAINST FUCHS

12.

IN LEONARDUM FUCHSIUM APOLOGIA Original ed.
[Lyons] 1536

Title (Fig. 19): In Leonardum Fuchsium apologia, autore Michaele Villanovano. [Printer's device] 1536.

Collation: 8vo. A⁸; 8 unnumb. *ll.*

Note: Through the printer's devices on the title-page and on the verso of the final leaf, the book has been identified as from the press of Gilles Huguetan who printed at Lyons from 1527 to 1544. The work, however, was not known to Baudrier. This brief polemic was undertaken in behalf of Symphorien Champier who was having his differences of opinion with Fuchs on the relative merits of the Galenical *versus* the Arabic approach to medicine. Although it is essentially a medical treatise (his first), Servetus could not resist seizing the opportunity to attack Fuchs, a Lutheran sympathizer, on the matter of justification by faith.

    Tollin in one of his many papers about Servetus ("Michael Servet's brevissima apologia pro Symphoriano Campegio in Leonardum Fuchsium" in the *Deutsches Archiv für Geschichte der Medizin,* 1884, *7,* 409–442) reprints the text of the Apologia through the second line of Aiiiib. This is taken from pages 50–54 of Sebastian Montuus' *Dialexeon medicinalium libri duo* (Lugduni, sub scuto Basiliensi apud Michaelem Parmanterium, 1537) because, Tollin says, Servetus' book itself has been lost (for some reason he seems not to have known of the copy in the Bibliothèque Nationale). In Montuus' rendering the Greek words which are absent in the only copies now known are given, indicating that he must either have had a copy in which they appeared or else interpolated them himself. It seems rather improbable that the printer who set the text of the pamphlet would not have had the necessary Greek fonts, and more intriguing to imagine, as Professor O'Malley suggests, that, the Greek not being really necessary, the blanks were left as a thrust at Fuchs who was criticized for the unnecessary larding of his text with both Greek and Latin.

Copies: London,² Paris.⁴ The Reverend Alexander Gordon (1841–1931) told Leonard L. Mackall some time before 1914 that he had learned of another copy in private possession, but he did not disclose the name of the owner.

Copy used: Dr. Williams's Library.

13.

IN LEONARDUM FUCHSIUM APOLOGIA Facsimile
[Oxford, 1909]

Title: [As in No. 12].

Note: This fine example of collotype reproduction was done by the Oxford University Press from the copy in Dr. Williams's Library, London. The date of the reproduction is given by Dr. Gordon in his excellent account of Servetus in the *Encyclopedia Britannica* (11th ed.).

Copies: London,²,⁴,⁶,⁷ Oxford,¹ Upsala.² CaTAM, CSt-L, CtY-M, Dibner (2), DSG, IEN-M, MdBJ-W, MBM, MnU, NNC, NNNAM, PPCP.

Copy used: Yale.

❧IN LEONARDVM❧
FVCHSIVM APOLOGIA.
Autore Michaele Villanouano.

✤

*D: Williams's Library
London .*

1536

Fig. 19. Title-page of *In Leonardum Fuchsium apologia,* 1536. (Reproduced through the courtesy of Dr. Williams's Library, London).

14.

IN LEONARDUM FUCHSIUM APOLOGIA English trans.
Philadelphia, 1953

Title: The apology against Fuchs (1536). *In:* Michael Servetus. A translation of his geographical, medical and astrological writings . . . by Charles Donald O'Malley. Philadelphia, American Philosophical Society, 1953.

Collation (entire volume): 8vo. 208 pp.

Contents: pp. 38-42 introduction, p.[43] photograph of copy of 1536 edition in Dr. Williams's library, pp. 44-54 translation of text.

Note: This is the third of Servetus' writings to be translated into English. The work in which it appears is Volume 34 of the Memoirs of the American Philosophical Society and also carries the number 32 of the Monograph Series of the Department of the History of Medicine of Yale University. It was printed in England under the auspices of Lloyd-Luke (Medical Books) Ltd. of London.

V. THE SYRUPS

15.

SYRUPORUM UNIVERSA RATIO Original ed.   *Paris, 1537*

Title (Fig. 20): Syruporum universa ratio, ad Galeni censuram diligenter expolita. Cui, post integra de concoctione disceptationem, praescripta est vera purgandi methodus, cum expositione aphorismi: Concocta medicari. Michaële Villanovano authore. [Three lines of Greek] Parisiis Ex officina Simonis Colinaei. 1537.

Collation: 8vo. a–h⁸, i⁷; 70 + [1] *ll.*

Contents: a1*a* title, a1*b* blank; a2 Ad Lectores (in italic type); a3*a*–i6*b* text; i7*a* errata, i7*b* blank.

Note: At the time this book appeared, Servetus had had little formal medical education, but he had undoubtedly been exposed to a good deal of medicine in his association with Champier. Osler (see footnote 11) states that he had helped Champier with his French *Pharmacopoeia* and had thus gained some familiarity with the subject. He displays considerable knowledge of Galen's writings and discusses at length the Galenical theory of the value of syrups in digestion (that they are useless) as opposed to that of Avicenna and the Arabists who placed great faith in their curative value. He spends most of the book outlining these two opposing theories, and only in the fifth and sixth chapters does he give the composition and use of the syrups, reaching the conclusion that they had their place in the treatment of disease but should be used sparingly.

Copies: Budapest, Cambridge,[2,4] Edinburgh,[1] Geneva, Glasgow, Göttingen, London,[1,2,4,7] Milan, Montpellier, Munich,[1] Paris,[1,3,4,8] Rome, Upsala.[2] CSt-L, CtY-M, DSG, MBM, MdBJ-W, NNC.

Copy used: Yale, purchased by Dr. Cushing from Taeuber and Weil at Munich, August 1931.

16.

SYRUPORUM UNIVERSA RATIO Second ed.   *Venice, 1545*

Title (Fig. 21): Syruporum universa ratio, ad Galeni censuram diligenter expolita: [3 lines as in previous entry] Michaele Villanovano authore. [Printer's device] Venetiis. Ex officina Erasmiana apud Vincentium Valgrisium. M. D. XLV.

Collation: 8vo. Italic type; a–h⁸; 63 + [1] *ll.*

Contents: a1*a* title, a1*b* blank; a2 Ad lectores; a3*a*–h7*b* text; h8*a* blank, h8*b* printer's device.

Note: This is the only one of Servetus' writings to have an Italian imprint—and that during his life-time. How it happened to have been reissued after an interval of eight years is not known, at least to this compiler, but the revival of interest in the tract was to continue actively for the next three years.

Syruporum vni-
VERSA RATIO, AD GA-
leni cenſuram diligenter
expolita.

Cui, poſt integrā de concoĉtione diſceptationem,
præſcripta eſt uera purgandi methodus, cum expoſitione aphoriſmi: Concoĉta medicari.

Michaële Villanouano authore.

Πρὸς τὸμ φιλίατρομ.
Εὔροα ποιήσωμ τάτε σώμαῖα, τάτε πεπάνωμ
Ωμὰ χυμῶμ, τάυτης δ'όγματα ἴϑι βίβλυ.

PARISIIS
Ex officina Simonis Colinæi.
I 5 3 7

Fig. 20. Title-page of the first edition of *Syruporum
universa ratio*, Paris 1537.

SYRVPORVM
VNIVERSA RATIO,
AD GALENI CENSVRAM
DILIGENTER EX=
POLITA:

Cui, post integram de concoctione disceptationem, præscripta est uera purgandi methodus, cum expositione aphorismi:Concocta medicari. MICHAELE Villanouano authore.

VENETIIS.

Ex officina ERASMIANA apud Vin= centium Valgrisium.

M. D. XLV.

Fig. 21. Title-page of the second edition of the *Syrups*, issued at Venice in 1545.

Copies: Augsburg, Basel, Bonn, Cambridge,[4] Cracow, Erlangen, Göttingen, Leipzig, London, [1,5,7] Manchester,[2] Milan, Munich,[1] Paris, [3,4,6] Rome,[1] Upsala,[2] Venice, Vienna.[1] CaMM-Os, CtY-M, Dibner, NIC, PPCP.

Copy used: Yale, from the library of Arnold C. Klebs. Dr. Cushing had a copy also, from the Graf Stolberg library, which was sold as a duplicate.

17.

SYRUPORUM UNIVERSA RATIO Third ed.   *Lyons, 1546*

Title (Fig. 22): [Wording the same as in previous entry] [Printer's device] Lugduni, apud Gulielmum Rovilium, M. D. XLVI.

Colophon: Excudebat Lugduni Ioannes Pullonus, aliàs de Trin.

Collation: 8vo. Mostly in italic type (quotations in Roman). A-G^8; 111 pp.

Contents: A1*a* title, A1*b* blank; A2 Ad lectores; A3*a*-G8*a* text, G8*b* blank.

Note: This, the first of the three Lyons printings, was reëdited by Servetus during his residence at Vienne. It is the edition that was used for the Spanish translation in 1943.

Copies: Bordeaux, Frankfurt am Main, Göttingen, London,[1] Madrid, Paris,[4,7] Rome,[1] Upsala,[1] Vienna.[1] CtY-M, DSG, NNNAM.

Copy used: Yale, in the bequest of Harvey Cushing. It came from the library of the famous French chemist, François-Vincent Raspail, and has his book-stamp on the title-page. A copy also came to the Library in the bequest of Arnold C. Klebs; it was uncut, measuring 16.1 by 11 cm., and was on heavier paper, but it was badly stained throughout. It has been sold as a duplicate.

18.

SYRUPORUM UNIVERSA RATIO Fourth ed.   *Lyons, 1547*

Title: [Same as preceding edition] M. D. XLVII.

Collation, contents, and colophon: [Same as in No. 17].

Note: This is merely a reissue of No. 17.

Copies: Oxford,[1] Paris,[6] Upsala.[2] DSG, MBM.

Copy used: Boston Medical Library, measuring 15.6 by 10.4 cm. No provenance; newly bound in old soft vellum music sheet. Sig. G3 is bound before G2, but this may be purely fortuitous. No other copy examined.

19.

SYRUPORUM UNIVERSA RATIO Fifth ed.   *Lyons, 1548*

Title: [Same as preceding edition.] M. D. XLVIII.

Collation, contents, and colophon: [Same as in No. 17].

SYRVPORVM
VNIVERSA RATIO,
AD GALENI CENSV
RAM DILIGEN=
TER EXPO=
LITA.

*

*Cui, poſt integram de concoctione diſceptationem,
præſcripta eſt uera purgandi methodus,
cum expoſitione Aphoriſmi:
Concocta medicari,* M I=
CHAELE Villa=
*nouano au=
thore.*

REM MAXIMAM SIBI   PROMITTIT PRVDENTIA.

LVGDVNI, APVD GVLIEL=
MVM ROVILIVM,
M. D. XLVI.

Fig. 22. Title-page of the first of three Lyons editions of
the *Syrups,* 1546.

Note: The entry for this edition is given by Baudrier (Vol. IX, p. 148), who states that it is reissued from the edition of 1546.

Copies: No copy traced.

20.

SYRUPORUM UNIVERSA RATIO ? Sixth ed.   *Venice,* 1548

Note: In his account of Servetus in the *Encyclopedia Britannica,* the Reverend Alexander Gordon states that the 'Syrups' was issued for a second time at Venice in 1548. This statement was also made by van der Linde (1891, p. 54) and by Wilbur (1932), van der Linde giving the same printer as for the 1545 edition. However, in his more recent (1950) work, Wilbur does not mention this second Venice edition but adds 1548 to the years of the Lyons printings. It is therefore possible that there has been some confusion as to place of publication of the 1548 edition, although Venice cannot be entirely ruled out. To date no copy has been traced.

21.

SYRUPORUM UNIVERSA RATIO Spanish trans. *Madrid,* 1943

Title: Razón universal de los jarabes según inteligencia de Galeno por Miguel Villanovano (Miguel Serveto). Con un prólogo del Dr. Nicasio Mariscal y Garcia de Rello, Académico de Número. Madrid, Imprenta de J. Cosano . . . 1943.

Title preceding translation [p.303]: Razón universal de los jarabes, según inteligencia de Galeno diligentemente expuesta. A la cual se añade, despues de la integra disertación acerca de la concocción, el verdadero método de purgar, con exposición del aforismo "Condocta medicari." Autor Miguel Villanovano (Miguel Serveto). Leon de Francia.—En casa de Guillermo Rovilio.—MDXLVI. Traducida al Español por el Dr. J. Goyanes Capdevila, Académico y bibliotecario de la Academia Nacional de Medicina, con la colaboración de D. Jaime Torrubiano Ripoll, Doctor en Teología y Derecho canónico. Madrid.—Imp. de J. Cosano.—1935 [*sic*].

Collation: 8vo. 484 pp., 1 *l.*

Contents: p.[1] series half-title; p.[3] series title; p.[5] title, pp.[7]-8 Advertencia preliminar; p.[9] title-page for Dr. Mariscal's paper ("Participación que tuvieron los médicos españoles en el descubrimiento de la circulación de la sangre"); p.[11] photograph of Servetus, pp.[13]-215 text of Dr. Mariscal's paper; p.[216] illustration; pp.[217]-285 explanation of illustrations, pp.[287]-302 appendices, being translations into Spanish of passages from *Christianismi restitutio* and *Dialogorum de Trinitate libri duo;* p.[303] title-page for the 'Syrups'; p.[305] reproduction of title-page of Lyons 1546 edition, pp.[307]-[473] translation, pp.[475]-484 index, p.[485] colophon.

Note: This is Volume IX of the series, "Biblioteca clásica de la medicina Española," issued by the Academia Nacional de Medicina, and, as the title to the translation indicates, is based on the third edition of the work published at Lyons in 1546.

Copies: No census taken.

22.

SYRUPORUM UNIVERSA RATIO English trans.

Philadelphia, 1953

Title: The syrups (1537). *In:* Michael Servetus. A translation of his geographical, medical and astrological writings . . . by Charles Donald O'Malley. Philadelphia, American Philosophical Society, 1953.

Collation (entire volume): 8vo. 208 pp.

Contents: pp. 54-58 introduction; p.[59] photograph of title-page of 1537 edition; pp. 58-167 text.

Note: This, the most important of Servetus' medical writings, is (as pointed out in the note to No. 15) strictly Galenical in point of view but nevertheless gives the reader, especially the physiologist, some idea of the medical thought of that era. (For details of the volume in which it appeared see note to No. 14.)

VI. DISCOURSE IN FAVOR OF ASTROLOGY

23.

DISCEPTATIO PRO ASTROLOGIA First ed.   [*Paris, 1538*]

Title (Fig. 23): [None; begins] Michaelis Villanovani in quendam medicum apologetica disceptatio pro astrologia. [No place, no date—Paris,
1538.]

Collation: 8vo. 8 *ll.* without signature, foliation, or pagination.

Note: With the Ptolemy and the Syrups already to his credit, Michael Villanovanus was
undoubtedly well known in academic circles. His boundless energy and disputatious char-
acter, not to mention his probable need for funds, made lecturing a natural pursuit for him.
He was not one to be deterred by the fact that a Master's degree was a prerequisite for such
a pursuit; and if the faculty ever had any inclination to overlook this fact, they certainly
had no intention of doing so in the case of lectures in the field of judicial astrology. Warned
by Tagault, the Dean of the medical faculty, that such lectures were forbidden, Servetus
rushed about to find someone to put into print a statement in support of his case. As would
therefore be expected, the pamphlet was hastily prepared and set up on an unidentified press,
and subsequently as many copies as possible were confiscated.

Copies: Paris.[4,5]

Copy used: Bibliothèque Nationale, in photograph.

24.

DISCEPTATIO PRO ASTROLOGIA Tollin reprint *Berlin, 1880*

Title: Michaelis Villanovani (Serveti) in quendam medicum apologetica
disceptatio pro astrologia. Nach dem einzig vorhandenen echten Pariser
Exemplare, mit einer Einleitung und Anmerkungen neu herausgegeben
von Henri Tollin, Lic. theol., Prediger in Magdeburg. Berlin, C., 1880.
Verlag von H. R. Mecklenburg. . . .

Collation: 8vo. 45 pp., 1 *l.*

Contents: p.[1] title, p.[2] copyright, p.[3] dedication to Don Pedro
Gonzalez de Velasco, p.[4] blank; pp.[5]-20 introduction; pp.[21]-45
text of the Discourse; final leaf, advts.

Note: Henri Tollin has probably written more articles about Servetus than any other one
person—Bainton (1932) lists 75 titles. In the present brochure he is the usual warm supporter
of Servetus, and having found a copy of the unique *Disceptatio* in Paris, he gives a full Latin
transcription of the paper, adding many explanatory footnotes.

Copies: Basel, Cambridge,[2,4] Copenhagen,[2] Göttingen, Halle, Heidelberg, Jena, Leipzig,
London,[1] Munich,[1,2] Oslo, Oxford,[1] Paris,[4] Rome,[1] Strasbourg, Stuttgart,[1] Tübingen, Upsala,[2] Utrecht, Vienna[1,2]. CaMM-Os, CtY-M, DSG, MdBJ-W, MdBM, MoSW-M, NNN

❧ MICHAELIS

VILLANOVANI IN QVEN·
dam medicum apologctica difce-
ptatio pro Aftrologia.

I Nterpellauit lectiones meas, cum Lute
tiæ Aftronomiam publice profiterer ,
Medicus quidam, duabus rationibus eã
totam, tam parte illa,quæ ex aftris præ-
dicit , quam alia,quæ cœleftes motus in
ftrumentis obferuat , fubuertere conatus. Quibus
nil aliud plane , quam fuam infcitiam prodidit ,
imperitum alium fequutus , fub quo præceptore
fuerat rude donatus , vt temere ambo dãnĕt quæ
penitus ignorant. Philofophos fe tamen ii , fi diis
placet , & medicos iactitãt, cũ a fuis ducibus, Pla
tone,& Ariftotele,Hippocrate & Galeno eos def-
ciuiffe ex hoc quiuis manifefto intellicat , quod
oĕs Aftrologiæ fuerint periti , quã hi nõ folum illi
fe egregie ignorare fatentur,fed & infectantur pe
tulanter. Illi Philofophiæ familiariffimã, hi aduer
fiffimã cõtend unt . Citabo itaqueprius eorũ au-
torum teftimonia , vtrique aftrologiæ parti fauen
tia, deinde ad rationes veniã. Diuinus igitur Plato in libro de regno , cœli circuitum effe mutati-
onis horum inferiorum caufam oftĕdit. Et in epi
nomide, nolite, inquit, ignorare aftronomiã fapiĕ
tiffimum quiddã effe : ibique docet grecos eã ..b
ægyptiis didiciffe.& i dialogo feptimo de legibus
folem & lunã magnos deos appellat. I꜠ Timæo ,

Fig. 23. First page of the *Disceptatio pro astrologia* printed at
Paris in 1538. (Courtesy of the Bibliothèque Nationale, Paris).

AM, NNUT. An English translation of the Servetus tract (unpublished) is at the Library of the Union Theological Seminary, New York, having been made for Samuel Macaulay Jackson in 1910.

Copy used: Yale, sent to the Library from Geneva in 1950 by Dr. R. B. Livingston; in paper wrappers.

25.
DISCEPTATIO PRO ASTROLOGIA English trans.
Philadelphia, 1953

Title: The discourse in favor of astrology. *In:* Michael Servetus. A translation of his geographical, medical and astrological writings . . . by Charles Donald O'Malley. Philadelphia, American Philosophical Society, 1953.

Collation (entire volume): 8vo. 208 pp.

Contents: pp. 168-171 introduction; p. [172] first page of tract; pp. 173-188 text.

Note: Henry Tollin, although he rescued this rare little tract from obscurity, did not undertake its translation into German when he issued his paper on the subject in 1880. The translation into English by Mr. O'Malley is therefore the first to see the light.

VII. THE HOLY BIBLE

26.
BIBLIA SACRA Folio ed.   *Lyons, 1542*

Title (Fig. 24): Biblia sacra ex Santis Pagnini tralatione, sed ad Hebraicæ linguæ amussim novissimè ita recognita, & scholiis illustrata, ut planè nova editio videri possit. Accessit præterea liber interpretationum Hebraicorum, Arabicorum, Græcorumque nominum, quæ in sacris literis reperiuntur, ordine alphabetico digestus, eodem authore. [Printer's device] Lugduni, Apud Hugonem à Porta. M. D. XLII. Cum privilegio ad annos sex.

Colophon: Lugduni, Excudebat Gaspar Trechsel: Anno M. D. XLII.

Collation: Fol. ★⁶, a-z⁸, A-B⁸, C¹⁰, D-K⁸, L⁴, Aa-Dd⁸, E⁶; [6] *ll.,* 269 (wrongly numbered from 225 onward), [39] *ll.*

Contents: Fol. ★1a title, ★1b blank; ★2a Michaël Villanovanus lectori S., ★2b-3a Joannes Nicolaus Victorius omnibus sacrarum literarum candidatis S.; ★3b-6b Pagnino's prologue; a1a-C10a Old Testament, C10b blank; D1a-L3b New Testament, L4 Santes Pagninus to Thomas Sartinus; Aa1a-Ee5b Liber interpretationum Hebraicorum Græcorumque nominum; Ee6a Errata & Colophon, Ee6b blank.

Note: The editing of this Bible must have been work that brought Servetus much pleasure, and at the end of his note to the Reader he gives thanks "first to Almighty God, and then to Hugues de la Porte, citizen of Lyons, through whose efforts and expense this has been published." Willis calls attention to the fact that there is little evidence that Servetus made use of Pagnino's MS. notes in the 1528 edition but rather that he followed the reprint from this made by the scholarly publisher at Cologne, Melchior Novesianus, in 1541. Be that as it may, Servetus' comments reflect his wide reading and restless intellect, and Calvin's sneering remark that it was "thievish in the editor when he took five hundred livres in payment for the vain trifles and impious follies with which he encumbered almost every page of the book" is scarcely justified.

Copies: Brussels, Cambridge,³ Dublin, Glasgow, Leiden, Lisbon, London,¹·² Madrid, Manchester,¹ Montpellier, Oxford,¹ Paris,⁴·⁵·⁷ Parma, Tübingen, Zürich. CaMM-Os, CBPac, Ct-Y, MdBJ-W, NIC, NN, NNP.

Copy used: Yale, measuring 34 by 24 cm.

27.
BIBLIA SACRA Octavo ed.   *Lyons, 1542*

Title (Fig. 25): Biblia sacra ex postremis doctorum omnium vigiliis, ad Hebraicam veritatem, & probatissimorum exemplarium fidem. Cum

BIBLIA

ſacra ex Santis Pagnini trala-
TIONE, SED AD HEBRAI-
cæ linguæ amuſſim nouiſsimè ita recognita, &
ſcholiis illuſtrata, ut planè noua editio uideri poſsit.

*Acceßit præterea Liber interpretationum Hebraicorum, Arabicorum, Græcorumʠ̃
nominum, quæ in ſacris literis reperiuntur, ordine alphabetico digeſtus, eodem authore.*

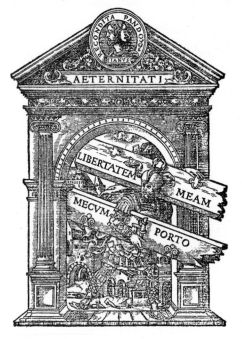

LVGDVNI,
Apud HVGONEM à Porta.
M. D. XLII.

Cum priuilegio ad annos ſex.

Fig. 24. Title-page of the Pagnini Bible edited by Servetus, 1542.
(Kindness of Yale University Library).

BIBLIA

S A C R A,

Ex poſtremis Doctorum omnium
uigiliis, ad Hebraicam ueri͑
tatem, & probatiſsi͑
morum exem͑
plarium fi͑
dem.

Cum Argumentis, Indice, & He-
braicorum nominum interpretatione.

L V G D V N I,
Apud Hugonem à Porta,
1 5 4 2.

Fig. 25. Title-page of the octavo Bible corrected by Servetus, 1542.

argumentis, indice, & Hebraicorum nominum interpretatione. [Printer's device] Lugduni, Apud Hugonem à Porta. 1542.

Colophon (Rr8*b*): Gaspar Trechsel excudebat Viennæ.

Collation: 8vo. Double column with marginalia. ¶[8], a-z[8], A-Z[8], Aa-Rr[8]; 500 + [4] *ll.*

Contents: ¶1*a* title, ¶1*b* Ad sacrarum literarum studium exhortatio ex sacris literis; ¶2*a*-4*b* Index testimoniorum a Christo & Apostolis Novo testamento citatorum ex veteri. . .; ¶5*a*-8*a* Hieronymi prologus Galeatus; ¶8*b* Prologus; a1*a*-Dd8*b* (*ll.*1-400) Old Testament text; Ee1*a*-Rr4*a* (*ll.*[401]-500 New Testament; Rr4*b*-6*b* Hebraicorum, Chaldeorum, Græcorúmque nominum interpretatio; Rr7 Summa totius Sacræ scripturæ, librorum videlicet veteris & novi Testamenti; Rr8*a* Ordo librorum, Rr8*b* Colophon.

Note: This edition of the Bible does not contain any internal evidence of having been edited by Servetus, but Baudrier (1921, XII, 256) lists it under the publications of Gaspard Trechsel with the comment: "Edition fort rare, corrigée par Michel de Villeneuve [Servet]." Mackall in his note on the flyleaf of the copy in the New York Public Library states that Baumgarten in 1754 first suggested (*Nachrichten von merkwürdigen Büchern,* V, 378) that Servetus had probably edited the octavo edition, and Copinger in 1892 (*Incunabula Biblica,* no. 297) could locate only the copy at Stuttgart.

Copies: Geneva, Stuttgart;[2] NN, 'American private collection.' This information comes from Gerald D. McDonald's article, "The Servetus octavo Bible, Lyons, 1542, given to the Library" (*New York Public Library Bulletin,* 1935, *39,* 931-2).

Copy used: New York Public Library, measuring 17 by 11.2 cm.; the gift of L. L. Mackall. It is bound in modern vellum, with the bookplate of Sir Thomas Brooke whose library was sold at Sotheby's in 1913.

28.

BIBLIA SACRA Seven-vol. ed.   *Lyons,* 1545

Title: Biblia sacra cum glossis, interlineari & ordinaria, Nicolai Lyrani postilla & moralitatibus, Burgensis additionibus, & Thoringi replicis. . . . Omnia ad Hebræorum & Græcorum fidem iam primum suo nitori restituta, & variis scholiis illustrata. Lugduni, Anno M. D. XLV. Cum privilegio Regis.

Colophon (Vol. VII, sig. v5*b*): Lugduni, ex officina Gaspari Trechsel, M. D. XLV.

Collation: Fol., in 2 columns, 7 vols.: I, 377 + [1] *ll.,* II, 315 + [1] *ll.,* III, 440 *ll.,* IV, 479 + [1] *ll.,* V, 244 + [1] *ll.,* VI, 285 + [1] *ll.,* VII, 156 unnumb. *ll.* (sig. a-s[8], t-v[6]).

Contents: Vols. I-IV contain the books of the Old Testament, Vols. V-VI those of the New Testament. Vol. VII is the alphabetical index.

Note: Baudrier (1921, XII, 257–62) describes these volumes at length and also reprints from his 1913 paper the transcript of the curious agreement between Servetus and the members of the Company of Publishers of Lyons dated 14 February 1540. Therein are listed in detail his duties in connection with the publication: the preparation of the index volume, the various tasks of a proof reader and editorial consultant, etc. Thus it would appear that in this instance he played a far less important rôle, and the edition may be included here principally on the basis of his association with the project.

Copies: Baudrier lists Bordeaux (*théol.*), Florence, Geneva, Lyons, and Nantes. The present census has no record of any copies.

VIII. THE RESTORATION OF CHRISTIANITY

29.

CHRISTIANISMI RESTITUTIO First ed. *[Vienne]* 1553

Title (Fig. 6): Christianismi restitutio. Totius ecclesiæ apostolicæ est ad sua limina vocatio, in integrum restituta cognitione Dei, fidei Christi, iustificationis nostræ, regenerationis baptismi, et cænæ domini manducationis. Restituto denique nobis regno cœlesti, Babylonis impiæ captivitate soluta, et Antichristo cum suis penitus destructo. [line of Hebrew quotation ("And at that time shall Michael stand up"—Daniel 12:1) and one in Greek ("And there was war in heaven"—Revelation 12:7)] M. D. LIII.

Collation: 8vo. a-z⁸, A-Z⁸; 734 + [1] pp.

Contents: a1a title, a1b index; a2a-s7b De Trinitate divina . . . libri septem; s8a-z1b De fide et justitia regni Christi . . . libri tres; z2a-N8b De regeneratione superna, et de regno Antichristi, libri quatuor; O1a-T7b Epistolæ triginta ad Ioannem Calvinum Gebennensium concionatorem; T8a-Z7b De mysterio Trinitatis et veterum disciplina, ad Philippum Melanchthonem, et eius collegas, apologia; T8a errata, T8b blank.

Note: With this, his final work, as with his first publication, Servetus had difficulty when he came to look for a printer. An attempt to enlist the services of someone in Basel failed. Finally after some persuasion he got the consent of the publisher at Vienne, Balthazar Arnoullet, and of Guillaume Guéroult, Arnoullet's brother-in-law and director of his press, to print the volume. He asked that no indication of author, publisher, or place be given, and he promised to be responsible personally for the cost of printing and for correction of the proofs. The work was undertaken in great secrecy (each page of manuscript was destroyed as soon as it was printed), and three printers completed the task between 29 September 1552 and sometime early in January 1553. The books were then put in bales and sent to Lyons; five bales were held there (it is thought for later distribution in Italy), and the rest were consigned to two or three different persons for subsequent sale particularly at the Frankfort fair which at that time was the focal point for the distribution of books. However, when the true nature of the book's content was revealed and implication in its production had resulted in Arnoullet's imprisonment, he sent an urgent request to his agent at Châtillon, near Geneva, to have all copies in Frankfort destroyed. This was done most efficiently, but it is not known whether meanwhile any copies had actually been sold; there could not have been many. The five bales that had remained at Lyons were burned at Vienne on 17 June 1553 together with Servetus' effigy. Thus there remained only the few copies retained as evidence by the authorities.

The volume contains Servetus' proposals for the reformation of Christianity. It has particular interest for historians of medicine because of the passage in the fifth book of "De Trinitate divina" where Servetus, in discussing the Holy Spirit, used an example from anatomy to clarify his argument and thereby became the author of the first printed description of the lesser circulation of blood through the lungs. The passage remained completely buried for over a century until Charles Bernard, an English surgeon, gave William Wotton a tran-

scription of it which he had had in turn from an unnamed friend. Attention was called to
this by Wotton in his *Reflections upon ancient and modern learning* which was first published
at London in 1694. By 1697, when the second edition appeared, Wotton had actually seen
a MS. copy of the *Restitutio* (in the library of the Bishop of Norwich[46] and made from the
copy in the possession of the Landgrave of Hesse) and discussed the passages in greater detail, giving the pertinent Latin quotations from Servetus. In 1715 James Douglas in his
Bibliographiae anatomicae specimen also quoted the passage on the circulation, probably from
Wotton. By 1826 George Sigmond had seen a copy of Murr's reprint and in his *Unnoticed
theories of Servetus* he reprints several excerpts bearing on physiology (including those dealing with the circulation), stating that he wished to do so "in a correct and ungarbled form.
Dr. Wotton, M. de la Roche, Niceron, Chauffepié, have all quoted the passages either to
suit their own views, or to show merely the author's knowledge upon the circulation of the
blood." These passages on the circulation of the blood have subsequently been quoted,
translated, and paraphrased many times, and in the text above (pp. 37–40) the latest and
undoubtedly the best rendering by Professor O'Malley is given in full.

Copies: Edinburgh,[2] Paris,[4] Vienna.[1] Of the eight hundred or a thousand copies[47] printed,
only three are known to have survived, and at one time or another all were to be found
in Great Britain.

The Paris copy.[48] This volume, which has suffered from moisture, bears the name and
notes of Colladon, the friend and lawyer who served Calvin throughout Servetus' trial. It
contains manuscript notes in Latin written by Colladon which purport to be an index of
things in the book regarded as "impure" but which Mackall points out are no more than a
list of the headings in the book. The early history of this copy has not been traced satisfactorily. In a letter to Bishop Thomas Burnet under the date of 26 May 1706 Leibnitz refers
to a copy at Cassel in the library of the Landgrave of Hesse, but when the Landgrave sought
to find it in 1720 to show to Prince François-Eugène de Savoie-Carignan it had disappeared.
Cuthbertson quotes Chéreau to the effect that some twenty years later this copy was found
in the great library of Richard Mead. Somewhere between 1740 and 1745 Mead sent the
book to his close friend in Paris, Claude Gros de Boze, a fellow coin collector and member
of the Académie des Beaux-Arts, who gave him in exchange a series of rare medals and
coins. De Bose's library was sold after his death and another eminent collector, de Cottes,
bought the book for 1200 livres. He in turn sold it to a bibliophile named Gaignat from
whom the Duke de La Vallière purchased it in 1769 for 3810 livres. At the La Vallière sale
in 1783, the Bibliothèque Royale (later the Bibliothèque Nationale) bought the *Restitutio*
for 4120 livres.

The Edinburgh copy. This volume, now at the University of Edinburgh, is an imperfect
copy, lacking the first sixteen pages which are supplied in manuscript in a sixteenth century
hand and probably from an earlier draft of the book. The Reverend Alexander Gordon, a
most cautious and accurate Servetus scholar, believed that it must be the copy that had be-
longed to Calvin himself, and Cuthbertson gives the detailed evidence which leads him to
concur in this judgment. How it passed from Calvin's library to that of the Duke of Queens-
berry is not recorded, but it is from this latter source that the volume came in 1695 to be
deposited in the University.

The Vienna copy. This copy also had a peripatetic existence in its early days. The first

[46] Now in Cambridge University Library.
[47] D'Artigny (II,75) and Baudrier (1921, X,94) both say 800, but Servetus stated 1,000 in
his testimony at Geneva (*Opera Calvini*, VIII, 749).
[48] The best accounts of the Paris and Vienna copies are those of Mackall (footnote 17) and
the great French scholar, E. Doumergue, in the sixth volume (pp. 272–5) of his monumental
work, *Jean Calvin, les hommes et les choses de son temps* (Lausanne, 1899–1927, 7 vols.); more
recently the Vienna copy has been described by Herbert Hunger ("Michael Servet und das
Exemplar seiner Restitutio Christianismi in der Österreichischen Nationalbibliothek," *Biblos*,
1952, 1, 61–78).

known owner was a Transylvanian noble, Daniel Márkos Szent-Iványi (d. 1689), a follower of the Unitarian faith who was living in London in 1665. On returning to Hungary he presented his copy of the *Restitutio* to the congregation of Claudiopolis⁴⁹, of which he was a member. The minister of this Unitarian community, Stephan Agh, eventually gave it to the influential Count Samuel Teleki de Szék or Isek (1739–1822) in recognition of a favor which the Count had conferred upon the congregation at Cluj. When in 1786 Teleki learned of the great rarity and importance of the book, he presented it as a fitting gift to Emperor Joseph II who, it is believed, had tried in vain to buy the La Vallière copy two years previously. A short time later the Emperor deposited the book in the Imperial Library at Vienna. It was from this copy that Gottlieb von Murr made his reprint (see No. 34).

30.

CHRISTIANISMI RESTITUTIO Fragment   *Alba Julia,* 1569

Title (Fig. 26): De Regno Christi Liber primus. De Regno Antichristi Liber secundus. [ornament] Accessit tractatus de Pædobaptismo, et circuncisione. Rerum capita sequens pagella demonstrabit. Ioan.15.ver.14. Vos amici mei estis, si feceritis quæcunq̃ ego præcipio vobis. Albæ Juliæ. Anno domini 1569.

Collation: 4to. &⁴, (:)⁵, A-P⁴, Q⁵, R-Z⁴, AA-RR⁴, SS².

Contents: [&]1*a* title, [&]1*b* table of contents; &2*a*-(:)5*a* dedication to John II Sigismond, prince of Transylvania, King-elector of Hungary, (:)5*b* blank; A1 Preface; A2*a*-Q2*a* De regno Christi, Chapters 1-12; Q2*b* note by Biandrata announcing a later edition of other subjects; Q3 [missing]; Q4*a*-5*b* Notae membrorum regni Christi; R1-V4 De regno Antichristi et ejus mysteriis deque Paedobaptismo. Liber secundus. V4-BB3*b* Secunda pars. De Antichristi mysteriis; BB3*b*-CC3*b* Another passage, in which the Hebrew words are suppressed; CC4*a*-EE1 Signa sexaginta regni Antichristi, et revelatio eius, iam nunc praesens; EE4-KK1 De Paedobaptismo, pars tertia. De doctrina praecedente baptismum; KK1-SS2 arguments against paedobaptism which are not from Servetus.

Note: This anonymous volume was the work of Giorgio Biandrata (Lat. Blandrata), an Italian physician who became interested in the antitrinitarian movement. After taking his medical degree in 1533 at Montpellier (where he was a fellow student with Rabelais), he had become an authority on the diseases of women and because of his great reputation was called as personal physician to the Italian-born wife of King Sigismund of Poland and there he remained for about a decade before returning to Italy. Sometime after 1553 he was forced to leave Italy and subsequently Switzerland because of his religious sympathies, finally returning to Poland and Transylvania where his religious interests continued uppermost. Wilbur (1946, pp. 223 *et seq.*) and Kot (pp. 23 *et seq.*) give accounts of his activities, and Kot also gives a careful comparison of the text of Biandrata's *De regno Christi* with the *Restitutio.* The greater part of the description of the contents of the book given above is taken from this source as only the first 70-odd leaves have been available in photostat.

⁴⁹ The present-day Cluj in Rumania, and in the interim Klausenburg and Kolozsvár.

DE REGNO

CHRISTI LIBER

primus.

DE REGNO AN-

tichristi Liber secundus.

Accessit tractatus de Pædobaptismo, et Circuncisione.

Rerum capita sequens pagella demonstrabit.

Ioan.15.ver.14.
Vos amici mei estis, si feceritis quæcunq; ego præcipio vobis.

SERVETUS CASTRATUS.

Albæ Juliæ.
Anno domini 1 5 69.

Fig. 26. Title-page of the fragments from the *Christianismi restitutio* edited by Biandrata and issued in 1569. (Kindness of the British Museum).

Copies: According to Kot, there are copies at Cluj, Dresden, London,[1] Oxford,[1] Warsaw, and Wolfenbüttel.

Copy used: British Museum (photostats).

31.
CHRISTIANISMI RESTITUTIO Fragment   [*London*, 1723]

Title (Fig. 9): [None; begins] De Trinitate divina, quod in ea non sit invisibilium trium rerum illusio, sed vera substantiae Dei manifestatio in verbo, & communicatio in spiritu. Libri septem.

Collation: Large 4to (page proofs), gathered in twos. A-Z², Aa-Zz², Aaa-Rrr²; 252 pp.

Contents: pp. 1-2 Proemium, 'De homine Jesu Christo'; 3-39 Liber primus; 40-77 secundus; 78-105 tertius; 106-137 quartus; 138-173 quintus; 174-212 sextus; 213-245 septimus; 246-247 Proemium 'De Fide et Justitia Regni Christi'; 248-252 first part of Liber primus ending with the sentence, 'Paulus diende hanc fidem semper prædicavit' (p. 293 in original edition).

Note: This partial reprint (which never got beyond page proofs) has usually been attributed to Richard Mead, but Mackall (see footnotes 17, 29) states that there is no proof that Mead had a copy of the original edition before 1733. He offers no clue as to where the text for copying may have been secured.[50] To quote R. H. Hill (*Bodleian Quart. Record*, 1926–28, 5, 197), "Mr. Mackall found from the Public Records that the first five sheets were printed by Samuel Palmer, from copy supplied by Gysbert Dummer, a Dutchman; that Isaac Dalton printed the rest, also at the instance of Dummer, Peter Paris, a Frenchman, doing the composing; and that the correcting was done by one Patrick (probably Samuel Patrick the lexicographer), who called attention to the heretical nature of the work and caused it to be suppressed anew." The printing was thus interrupted in mid-stream, and the sheets were seized on 27 May 1723 on order of Dr. Gibson, Bishop of London.

The celebrated passage on the lesser circulation is to be found on pp. 144–6 (Nn2*b*-Oo1*b*) and is unchanged from the passage in the original 1553 edition.

Copies: Glasgow, London,[1,3] Oxford,[1,2] Paris.[4] Hill cites Edinburgh and Manchester as having copies, but these have not been verified in the present census. The British Museum has two copies, one in Freind's library. That at the Medical Society of London carries the bookplate of Dr. Richard Rawlinson. The Balliol-Bodleian copy is regarded as an earlier set of proofs than the others. It goes to page 260 (p. 302 of the original text, ending with 'Alia est in') and contains small directions or requests of the proof reader which are written in English, French, or Latin and which Mr. Hill says "bear witness to an international element in its production."

Copies used: British Museum, Oxford (microfilm).

[50] On the MS. copy of the *Restitutio* at the University of Edinburgh there is a pencilled note by Gerardus Meerman of Rotterdam (from whose library the MS. was purchased and given to the University sometime after 1856) which states that a few MS. copies were made from the Cassel volume. It is therefore possible that one of these was available to Dummer in 1723.

CHRISTIANI=
SMI RESTITV=
T I O.

Totius ecclefiæ apoſtolicæ eſt ad fua limina vocatio, in integrum reſtituta cognitione Dei, fidei Chriſti, iuſtificationis noſtræ, regenerationis baptiſmi, et cænæ domini manducationis. Reſtituto denique nobis regno cæleſti, Babylonis impiæ captiuitate foluta, et Antichriſto cum fuis penitus deſtructo.

בעת ההיא יעמוד מיכאל השר

καὶ ἐγένετο πόλεμος ἐν τῷ οὐρανῷ.

M.   D.   L I I I.

Fig. 27. Title-page of Murr's edition of *Christianismi restitutio* issued in 1790.

32.

CHRISTIANISMI RESTITUTIO Murr reprint [*Nuremberg*] 1790

Title (Fig. 27): [Same as No. 29.]

Final page of text gives date of printing in small characters (often misread 1791) at bottom of page, far below the author's identifying initials, M.S.V., and the original date, 1553.

Collation and Contents: Same as No. 29.

Note: Christoph Gottlieb (Theophilus) von Murr (1733–1811), a voluminous writer, translator, and bibliophile whom Mackall (see footnote 17) called "one of the last survivors of the now extinct species *Polyhistor*" brought out a page-for-page reprint from a manuscript transcribed from the Vienna copy. This MS. is now in the Harvard University Library (see footnote 37). Of this 1790 reprint Chéreau writes: "Il sera toujours facile de reconnaître cette réimpression: l'édition de Vienne a 33 lignes à la page; celle de Nuremberg en a 36 [or 37]; dans l'édition de Vienne les lignes ont 87 millimètres de longueur; dans l'édition de Nuremberg elles en ont 77; c'est-à-dire que l'imprimeur de Nuremberg ayant fait les lignes plus courtes que son confrère de Vienne, il en a augmenté le nombre pour que les pages se correspondissent exactement dans les deux éditions, et qu'à la rigueur on p t prendre ces dernières l'une pour l'autre. Il faut ajouter que l'*Errata* n'est pas le même, et que l'édition de 1553 offre dans les mots des abréviations qui ne sont pas dans celle de 1791 [*sic*]. Enfin le caractère typographique employé n'est pas le même." Chéreau (and others) state that the volume was printed by Rau.

Copies: Amsterdam, Augsburg, Basel, Bern, Bonn, Brussels, Cambridge,[3] Copenhagen,[1] Geneva, Glasgow, Göttingen, Grenoble, Halle, Heidelberg, Leipzig, London,[1,4,5,6] Madrid, Marburg, Munich,[1,2] Oxford,[1] Paris,[2,4,8] Parma, Rome,[1] Strasbourg, Stuttgart,[1] Tübingen, Upsala,[1,2] Vienna,[1,2] Warsaw, Zürich. CaMM-Os, CtY-M, DSG, Humbert, MBM, MH, MdBJ-W, NIC, NN, NNNAM, NNUT, PPCP, Trent. The copy at the Royal College of Obstetricians and Gynaecologists in London is Alexander Gordon's much annotated one. That at the Bibliothèque de l'Arsenal in Paris is from the library of the Duc de La Vallière. Dr. E. Weil (Cat. 16, no. 283, Oct. 1950) quoted a copy for £150.

Copy used: Yale; Charles Eliot Norton's copy, given by him in 1908 to George Foot Moore who in turn handed it on to Harvey Cushing in 1928.

33.

CHRISTIANISMI RESTITUTIO Polish fragment [*Pińczów*? 1568?]

Title: Okazanie Antychrysta y iego Krolestwa ze znaków iego własnych w słowie bożym opisanych, ktorych tu sześćdziesiat. [The advent of Antichrist and his kingdom, according to his own signs as described in the Word of God, of which there are sixty.]

Collation: 4to. 8 *ll.*

Note: This fragment was published without place or date, but Professor Wilbur (1932, 1950) assigned it with a query to Pińczów and 1568. According to Estreicher (*Bibliografia Polska*, Cracow, 1929, *27*, 409) it is a translation by Gregorius Paulus from the fifth part of the *Restitutio.* Paulus[51] does not venture to give either place or date for the tract nor does Bock

---

[51] For a brief account of Paulus see Wilbur (1946, p. 310, footnote 18).

(*Historia antitrinitariorum*, Leipzig, 1776, vol. 1, p. 619), but Stanislas Kot in his recent (1953) paper states (p. 28) that it was published in 1568 at Cracow at the same time that various other tracts by Paulus appeared.

Copies: There is reputed to be a copy in the Prince Czartorski Library at Cracow, but this fact has not been established in the present census. No other copy has been found.

There is another Polish fragment which has been listed as the work of Servetus: Rozdział Starego Testamentu od Nowego, żydowstwa od Chrześciaństwa, skad łatwie obaczysz prawie wyzystki roznice około wiary (The difference between the Old Testament and the New, from which you may easily see almost all the diversities in matters of faith). Bock mentions this, as does Wilbur (1950) who states that it is not now regarded as being by Servetus. Kot (1953) quotes Konrad Górski (*Grzegorz Pawel z Brzezin*. Cracow, Polish Academy of Sciences, 1929) who says definitely that he has examined the unique copy preserved at the Czartoryski Museum and that the text does not correspond with the respective chapter in the *Restitutio*.

34.

CHRISTIANISMI RESTITUTIO First German trans.

Wiesbaden, 1892–96

Title: Michael Servets Wiederherstellung des Christentums. Erster Band. [Zweiter Band, Dritter Band.] Wiesbaden. Verlag von Chr. Limbarth. 1892. [1895, 1896.]

Title of Vol. 1: Sieben Bücher über die Dreieinigkeit von Michael Servet zum erstenmal übersetzt durch Dr. Bernhard Spiess. . . . 1892.

Title of Vol. 2: Drei Bücher über den Glauben und die Gerechtigkeit des Reiches Christi, welche die Gerechtigkeit des Gesetzes übertrifft, und über die Liebe. Vier Bücher über die Wiedergeburt von oben und über das Reich des Widerchrists von Michael Servet zum erstenmal übersetzt durch Dr. Bernhard Spiess. . . . 1895.

Title of Vol. 3 (Ergänzungsband): Serveti De mysterio trinitatis et veterum disciplina ad Philippum Melanchthonem et eius collegas apologia im Originaltext herausgegeben von Dr. Bernhard Spiess. . . . 1896.

Collation: 8vo. 3 vols. [2] *ll.*, 323+ [1] pp.; [6] *ll.*, 304 pp.; [2] *ll.*, 60 pp.

Contents: Vol. 1: *l.*1a half-title, *l.*1b title of work; *l.*2a title of volume, *l.*2b copyright; pp. 1-2 translator's foreword, pp. 3-4 table of contents; p.[5] translation of original title, p.[6] transcription of original title; p.[7] half-title for the 'Seven Books' in German, p.[8] in Latin; pp.[9]-319 text, 320-323 notes; [324] advertisement of Limbarth's books.

Vol. 2: *l.*1a half-title, *l.*1b title-page of work; *l.* 2a title of volume, *l.* 2b copyright; *l.* 3 table of contents, *l.*4a translation of original title-page, *l.*4b transcription of same; *l.*5a half-title for 'Three Books' and 'Four Books', *l.*5b Latin of same; *l.*6a half-title for 'Three Books', *l.*6b blank, pp. 1-301 text, 302-304 concluding remarks of the translator.

Vol. 3: l. 1a half-title, *l.* 1b title of work; *l.* 2a title of volume, *l.* 2b copyright; pp. 1–56 text, pp. 57–60 concluding remarks of the translator.

Note: This is the only rendering of the *Christianismi Restitutio* that has yet been done in a modern European language. Vols. 1 and 2 are a translation of pp. 1–576 of the 'Restitutio' by Dr. Spiess. He omitted the thirty letters to Calvin and in the final volume reprints the last section of the 'Restitutio' in Latin.

Copies: London,[1] Manchester,[1] Munich.[2] NNUT (vol. 1 only).

Copies used: British Museum, Union Theological Seminary, New York.

35.
CHRISTIANISMI RESTITUTIO 2nd German ed., Vol. 1
Wiesbaden 1895

Title: [Same as No. 34 except for change of date to 1895 and addition of *Zweite Ausgabe.*]

Collation and Contents: Same as No. 35, Vol. 1.

Note: The designation, 'Zweite Ausgabe,' seems to appear only in Vol. 1, though it is more frequently than not bound with the supposedly 'first' editions of Vols. 2 and 3 (1895, 1896). In the copy which Mackall presented to the Welch Library he has written a note that this is merely a "Titel-Auflage" of the 1892 edition, i.e., original sheets with new title-pages only. He also states that Spiess withdrew his "Vorwort" from most copies of the second edition.

Copies: London;[1,4] CaMM-Os, MdBJ-W, NIC.

Copy used: Cornell University Library.

Chapter VI

SELECTED SOURCE MATERIALS

ALLWOERDEN, Henrik van. *Historia Michaelis Serveti* quam praeside Io. Lavr. Moshemio . . . Helmstadii, Stanno Bucholtziano [1727–28]. 7 p. l., 238 pp. "Scripta Serveti": pp. 162–237.

—*Historie van Michael Servetus den Spanjaart . . .* Uit de Latynsche en andere talen verduischt. . . . Rotterdam, J. D. Beman, 1729. xliv, 275, [11] pp. front. (port.)

ARTIGNY, Antoine Gachet d'. *Nouveaux mémoires d'histoire, de critique et de littérature*. Paris, 1749–56. 7 vols. [Vol. 2, pp. 35–154]

BAINTON, Roland H. The present state of Servetus studies. *J. modern Hist.*, 1932, *4*, 71–92.

—*Hunted heretic. The life and death of Michael Servetus, 1511–1553*. Boston, Beacon Press, 1953. xii, 270 pp.

BAUDRIER, H. L. *Bibliographie lyonnaise*. Recherches sur les imprimeurs, libraires, relieurs et fondeurs de lettres de Lyon au XVIᵉ siècle. Publiées et continuées par J. Baudrier. Lyon, L. Brun; Paris, A. Picard et Fils, 1895–1921. 12 vols.

BAUDRIER, J. Michel Servet: ses relations avec les libraires et les imprimeurs lyonnais. In: *Mélanges offerts à M. Emile Picot . . . par ses amis et ses élèves*. Paris, E. Rahir, 1913. 2 vols. [Vol. 1, pp. 41–56]

BAYON, Henry P. William Harvey, physician and biologist: his precursors, opponents and successors. *Ann. Sci.*, 1939, *4*, 65–106. [pp. 69–95]

—Calvin, Serveto, and Rabelais. *Isis*, 1947, *38*, 22–28.

BECKER, B., Ed. *Autour de Michel Servet et de Sebastien Castellion*. Haarlem, H.D. Tjeenk Willink & Zoon N.V., 1953. vii, 302 pp.

CASTRO y CALVO, José M. Contribución al estudio de Miguel Servet y de su obra "Syruporum." *Universidad*, Zaragoza, 1931, *8*, 797–830, 977–1030; 1932, *9*, 3–71.

CAVARD, Pierre. *Le procès de Michel Servet a Vienne*. Vienne, Syndicat d'Initiative, 1953. 173 pp.

CHAUFFEPIÉ, Jacques G. de. *The Life of Servetus*. Being an article of his Historical dictionary, Vol. IV. Printed at Amsterdam, Hague, and Leyden in the year 1756. Translated from the French by James Yair. London, R. Baldwin, 1771. xii, 212 pp.

CHÉREAU, Achille. *Histoire d'un livre. Michel Servet et la circulation pulmonaire*. Paris, G. Masson, 1879. 48 pp.

CUTHBERTSON, David. *A tragedy of the reformation,* being the authentic narrative of the history and burning of the "Christianismi restitutio,"

1553, . . . Edinburgh and London, Oliphant, Anderson & Ferrier, 1912. 66 pp. front. (port.), 6 facsim.

DRUMMOND, William H. *The Life of Michael Servetus, the Spanish physician, who, for the alleged crime of heresy, was entrapped, imprisoned, and burned, by John Calvin, the reformer, in the city of Geneva, October 27, 1553.* London, J. Chapman, 1848. xvi, 198 pp.

FLOURENS, Pierre. *Histoire de la découverte de la circulation du sang.* Paris, J. B. Baillière, 1854. viii, 216 pp. [pp. 11–17, 137–59, 202–14, these latter pages being the Latin text of the *Christianismi restitutio*, pp. 169–78). A second edition of Flourens' book appeared in 1857 (Paris, Garnier Frères), and it was translated into English by J. C. Reeve (Cincinnati, Rickey, Mallory & Co., 1859). In this edition the full Latin quotation is not given, but pertinent parts are introduced as footnotes in the text.

GOYANES, José. *Miguel Serveto, teólogo, geógrafo y médico, descubridor de la circulación de la sangre, quemado vivo en Ginebra en 1553: su vida y sus obras, sus amigos y enemigos.* Madrid, Hernando, 1933. 342 pp.

An impartial history of Michael Servetus, burnt alive at Geneva for heresie. London, Printed for A. Ward, 1724. 216 pp.

KNOTT, John F. Michael Servetus and the discovery of the circulation of the blood. *Med. Rec.*, 1911, *80*, 514–22.

KOT, Stanislas. L'influence de Michel Servet sur le mouvement anti-trinitarien en Pologne et en Transylvanie. In (pp. 72–115): Becker, B., *q.v.*

LADAME, Paul L. *Michel Servet, sa réhabilitation historique.* Genève, H. Kundig, 1913. 97 pp.

LINDE, Antonius van der. *Michael Servet, een brandoffer der gereformeerde inquisitie.* Groningen, P. Noordhoff, 1891. viii, 326 pp.

MOSHEIM, Johann L. von. *Anderweitiger Versuch einer vollständigen und unpartheyischen Ketzergeschichte.* Helmstaedt, bey Christian Friederich Weygand, 1748. 500 pp.

—*Neue Nachrichten von dem berühmten spanischen Arzte Michael Serveto, de zu Geneve ist verbrannt worden.* Helmstaedt, C. F. Weygand, 1750. 108 pp.

ODHNER, Carl T. *Michael Servetus, his life and teachings.* Philadelphia, J. B. Lippincott Co., 1910. v, 94 pp.

O'MALLEY, Charles D. *Michael Servetus. A translation of his geographical, medical and astrological writings with introductions and notes.* Philadelphia, American Philosophical Society, 1953. 208 pp.

SIGMOND, George. *The unnoticed theories of Servetus;* a dissertation addressed to the Medical Society of Stockholm. London: Printed for J. H. Burn, 1826. vi, 72 pp. (Second ed., London: Longman, Rees, Orme, Brown, & Green, 1828. v, 90 pp.)

Verwey, H. de la Fontaine. Reinier Telle, traducteur de Castellion et de Servet. In (pp. 142–157): Becker, B., *q.v.*

Wilbur, Earl Morse. *The two treatises of Servetus on the Trinity.* . . . Now first translated into English. Cambridge, Harvard University Press, 1932. xxxviii, 264 pp. [pp. vii–xxxvi]

—*A history of Unitarianism. Socinianism and its antecedents.* Cambridge, Mass., Harvard University Press, 1946. xiii, 617 pp. [pp. 49–75, 113–185]

—*A bibliography of the pioneers of the Socinian-Unitarian movement in modern Christianity in Italy, Switzerland, Germany, Holland.* Rome, Edizioni di Storia e Letteratura, 1950. 80 pp. (Sussidi Eruditi 1.)

Willis, Robert. *Servetus and Calvin, a study of an important epoch in the early history of the reformation.* London, H. S. King & Co., 1877. xvi, 541 pp.

Wright, Richard. *An apology for Dr. Michael Servetus:* including an account of his life, persecution, writings and opinions: being designed to eradicate bigotry and uncharitableness: and to promote liberality of sentiment among Christians. Wisbech, Printed and sold by F. B. Wright, 1806. xiv, [17]–458 pp.

Index of Names

MICHAEL SERVETUS · HUMANIST AND MARTYR BY
JOHN F. FULTON WAS PRINTED AT THE LANE PRESS
OF BURLINGTON · VERMONT IN AN EDITION
LIMITED TO SEVEN HUNDRED AND FIFTY COPIES

Reichner
6 July 1954.